Summer Book 1

for students entering first grade in the fall

by Angela M. Ankers, M. Ed.
Jodi Yarusinsky

Summerbook Company

ISBN: 978-1-933055-11-4

Printed in the United States of America

Summerbook Company
305 Lyndale Drive
Hartsville, SC 29550
(757) 678-4001
www.summerbookcompany.com

<u>Definitions and Helps</u>

A long vowel sound is the sound a vowel makes when it "says its name." Some examples
    are: a in ate   e in eel   i in island   o in over   u in use

A short vowel sound is the sound a vowel usually makes in a one syllable word.
    Some examples are: a in ant   e in exit   i in into   o in on   u in up

I Spy Something . . . . .

An object is pictured in the upper right-hand corner of each daily page. Examine
that object carefully, and then find it in the picture on the front or back cover.

How to Use This Book Effectively

1. Do one page a day in this book. If the page contains something difficult for your child, make sure he understands what he is doing. Do not allow him to guess his way through it. The answer key begins after page 50 for your convenience. You may wish to tear it out and store it in a separate place.

2. Do not become overly concerned if your child has difficulty with several exercises in this book. Reread the directions with him and help him do the first few. If he still does not understand, this may mean that he has already forgotten what he has learned and he really needs to work on this skill before first grade begins. It may also mean that the kindergarten curriculum did not introduce the skill. To decide which of these two reasons is the correct one, look through any old papers you may have. If you do not see any work similar to the exercise, I would recommend skipping all of the same type of exercises in the book unless you have the patience and desire to teach your child how to do them. Your child cannot "review" things he has never been taught.

3. Be patient and encouraging. It can be difficult to think about letters and numbers when it is sunny outside and a sibling is already playing in the pool.

4. Have your child read regularly, preferably daily. Your local library can provide an abundance of interesting stories for your child. We also have grade-appropriate books on our website, www.summerbookcompany.com.

5. Play the I Spy game. The visual tracking skills your child will practice are vital to his success in reading.

Add.

3+4 = _____   1+9 = _____   5+0 = _____

0+8 = _____   2+6 = _____   8+1 = _____

1+2 = _____   4+5 = _____   2+3 = _____

Count the objects.

_____   _____   _____

Write the letter for the first sound of the picture.

_____   _____   _____

- - - - -   - - - - -   - - - - -
_____   _____   _____

Circle the pictures that start with the /b/ sound.

Finish the line to connect the letters in order. Singing an alphabet song may help you.

A   M   N   P   W
B   V
C   L   O   Q   X
E   R   U
D   F   K   S   Y
I   T
G   H   J   Z

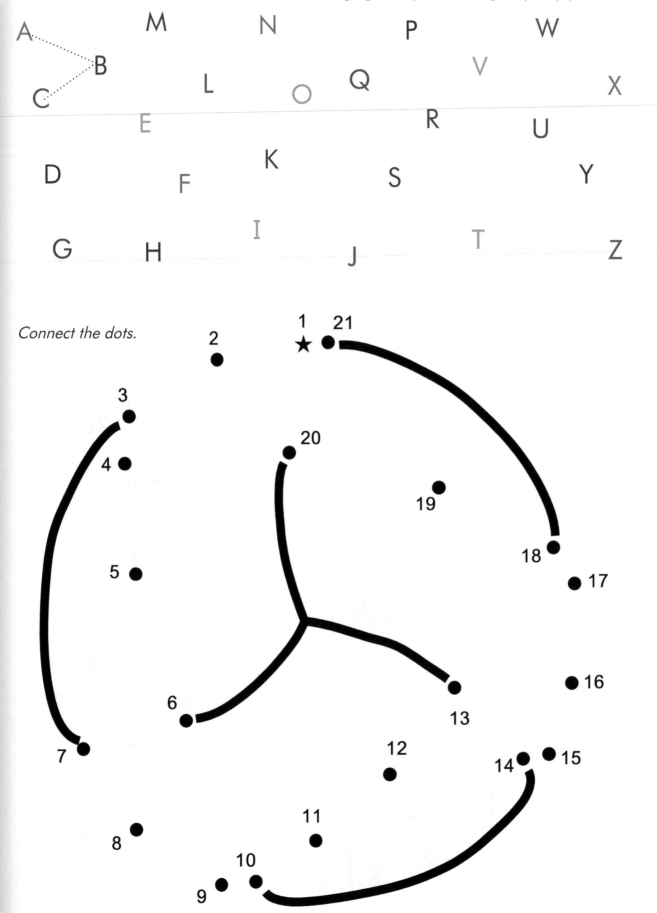

Connect the dots.

Tuesday

Count by ones.

1 ___ ___ ___ 5 ___ ___ ___ ___ 10 11

___ ___ ___ 15 ___ ___ ___ 19 ___

Circle the triangles.

Match the rhyming words.

fan	fill
hill	lap
tap	can

get	pop
top	dog
log	wet

Put an X on the pictures that do not end with the /l/ sound.

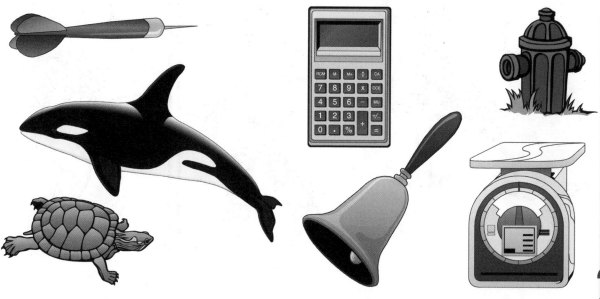

2

Which picture does not belong with the others? Why?

Add.

6	7	9	1	3	0	4	5	3
+ 2	+ 0	+ 1	+ 5	+ 7	+ 0	+ 2	+ 5	+ 1

What comes before and after each number?

_____ 3 _____   _____ 14 _____   _____ 10 _____

_____ 8 _____   _____ 19 _____   _____ 18 _____

_____ 6 _____   _____ 16 _____   _____ 11 _____

Circle the word that is the same as the first word in the row.

map	lap	map	mat
leg	leg	let	log
pin	pan	pit	pin

box	fox	bet	box
fun	fan	fun	fin
bat	ball	bit	bat

Match the word and the picture.

bag

fire

globe

truck

3

Use the numbers to color the picture.

1 - red   3 - blue   5 - orange

2 - yellow   4 - green   6 - purple

Thursday

Count by tens.

10 _____ _____ 40 _____ _____ 70 _____ 90 _____

_____ 20 _____ _____ 50 _____ _____ 80 _____ 100

Draw what comes next.

 _____   ↑↓↓↑↓↓ _____

 _____   abcabc _____

122122 _____   ◇◇◇◇ _____

Draw a picture of the word in the box.

cat	pan	tree

Circle the pictures that have the short /a/ sound in the middle of the word.

 4

Circle the sentence that tells about the picture.

Tad got it.

The cat is hot.

Ben can stack.

Ned can hop.

Bob is sad.

Pam can step.

A rat is not big.

Kim is not up.

Draw a line to help the bee get to the flowers.

Add.

6+3= _____   0+4= _____   2+1= _____

5+3= _____   1+7= _____   7+3= _____

4+4= _____   0+6= _____   5+1= _____

Circle the numbers that are the same as the first number in the row.

63	63	36	33	63
41	14	44	41	41
99	99	79	99	66

58	85	58	88	58
13	33	31	13	13
72	22	72	72	27

Match the upper and lower case letters.

A		y
Y		m
M		a

K		i
W		k
I		w

G		u
S		g
U		s

Put an X on the pictures that do not begin with the /h/ sound.

5

Connect the dots.

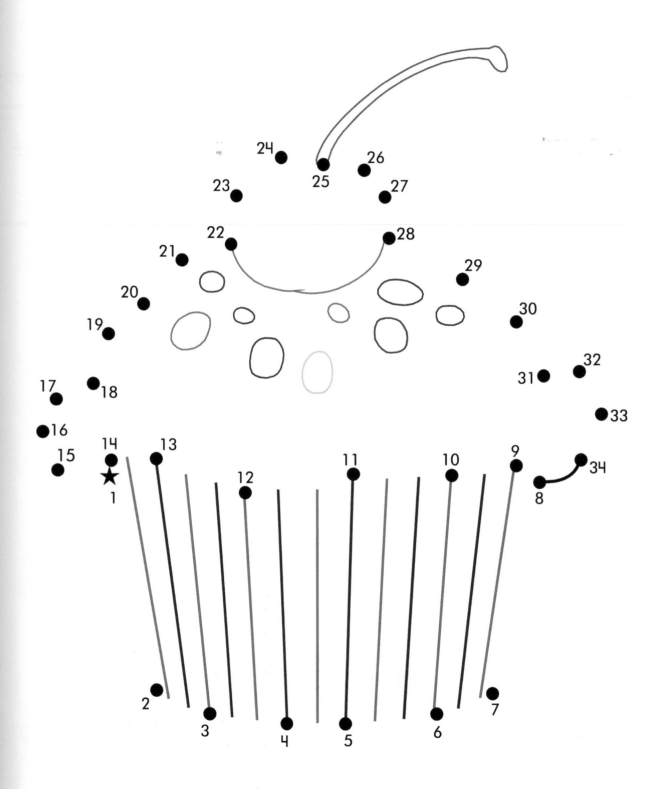

Monday

Add.

$$\begin{array}{ccccccccc}
1 & 3 & 8 & 2 & 7 & 0 & 4 & 1 & 6 \\
+1 & +0 & +2 & +5 & +1 & +2 & +3 & +3 & +4 \\
\end{array}$$

Color the correct number of objects.

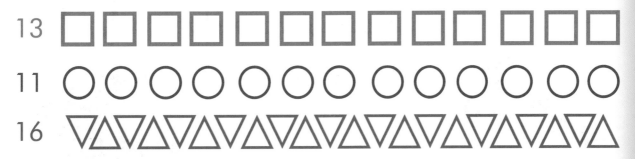

In each row, circle the letter that is different.

c	o	c	c
p	p	q	p
l	t	l	l

d	b	b	b
m	m	m	n
v	v	w	v

e	e	e	s
g	j	g	g
h	r	h	h

Circle the pictures that end with the /k/ sound.

6

Draw a line from each picture to the sentence that describes it.

Mom can fix a big ham.

Dad had a red pen.

A fat duck can quack.

Can Matt hit it?

Connect the dots.

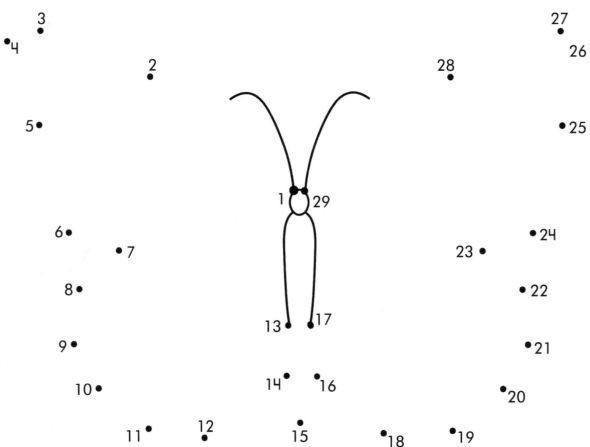

3

•4

2

27

26

28

5•

•25

6•

•7

•24

23 •

8•

•22

13• •17

9•

•21

10•

14• •16

•20

11• 12 15 •18 •19

29

1

Count by fives.

5 _____ 15 _____ _____ 30 _____ _____ 45 _____

5_____ _____ _____ 25 _____ _____ _____ _____ 50

Color the circles.

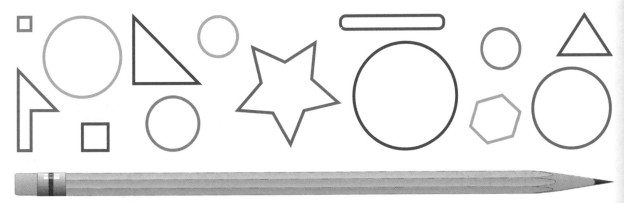

Write the capital letter next to the lower case letter.

_____ b   _____ n   _____ z

_____ l   _____ x   _____ j

_____ v   _____ h   _____ t

Put an X on the pictures that do not begin with the /u/ sound.

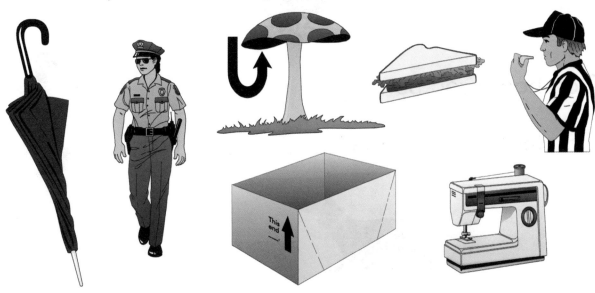

Read each rhyme and circle the word that should fill in the blank.

Ed had lots of fun.　　　　　　　sun

Ed ran and ran in the _____.　　tub

Ted is not a big lad.　　　　　　fed

Ben is the lad's _____.　　　dad

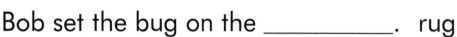

Bob got a red bug.　　　　　　nod

Bob set the bug on the _____.　rug

Dan had a sad pet.　　　　　　vet

Dan led the pet to the _____.　hop

Wednesday

Add.

2+0= _____   2+4= _____   6+4= _____

1+1= _____   0+3= _____   7+1= _____

0+6= _____   4+6= _____   0+1= _____

Write the number that comes before and after (counting by ones).

_____ 21 _____   _____ 30 _____   _____ 25 _____

_____ 38 _____   _____ 24 _____   _____ 26 _____

_____ 34 _____   _____ 23 _____   _____ 27 _____

Draw a picture of the phrase.

a sad lad	a big man	a red home

Match the rhyming pictures.

8

Fill in the missing numbers.

1	2		4	5	6	7	8	9	10
11	12	13	14	15	16		18	19	20
	22	23	24	25	26	27	28	29	30
31	32	33	34		36	37	38	39	40
41	42	43	44	45	46	47	48		50
51	52	53		55	56	57	58	59	60
61		63	64	65	66	67	68	69	70
71	72	73	74	75	76	77	78	79	
81	82	83	84	85	86	87		89	90
91	92	93	94	95		97	98	99	100

Thursday

Count by ones.

61 _____ _____ 64 _____ _____ 67 _____ 69 _____

71 _____ _____ 74 _____ _____ 77 _____ 79 _____

Circle the largest number in each row.

21	62	96
87	32	51
28	75	43

54	64	39
73	65	40
53	84	76

Write the letter for the last sound of the picture.

- - - - -   - - - - -   - - - - -

Circle the pictures that end with the /p/ sound.

9

Draw a line to the object that should come next. The first one is done for you.

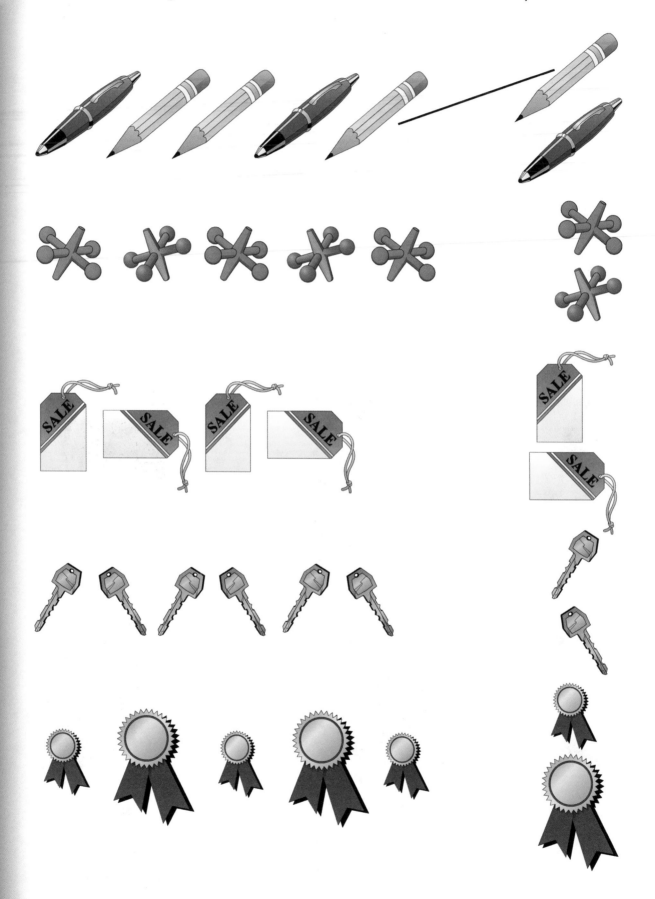

Add.

$$6 \quad 3 \quad 5 \quad 0 \quad 1 \quad 9 \quad 2 \quad 5 \quad 0$$
$$+4 \quad +2 \quad +0 \quad +7 \quad +4 \quad +1 \quad +8 \quad +4 \quad +0$$

Circle the shapes that have been divided in half.

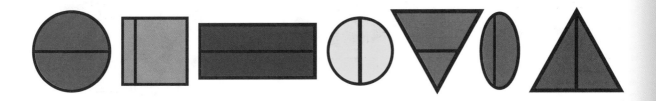

Choose one of the letters and write it on the line to make a word.

_____ ix
b   s

_____ ag
r   y

_____ um
f   g

_____ en
h   n

_____ ob
d   j

_____ ick
l   z

Put an X on the pictures that do not begin with the sound of /s/.

10

Circle the pictures of things that happen during the winter.

Monday

Add.

3+3= _____   0+9= _____   4+1= _____

4+6= _____   2+0= _____   7+2= _____

2+2= _____   2+8= _____   6+1= _____

Draw the correct number of balls in each box.

| 7 | 9 | 6 |

Circle the correct word.

grape   grapes   clock   clocks   tag   tags

Circle the pictures that begin with the sound of /n/.

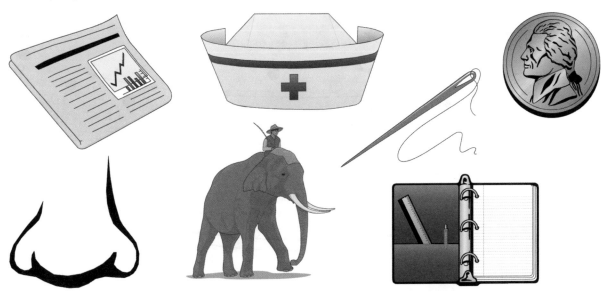

Color all the arrows pointing to the right.

Connect the dots.

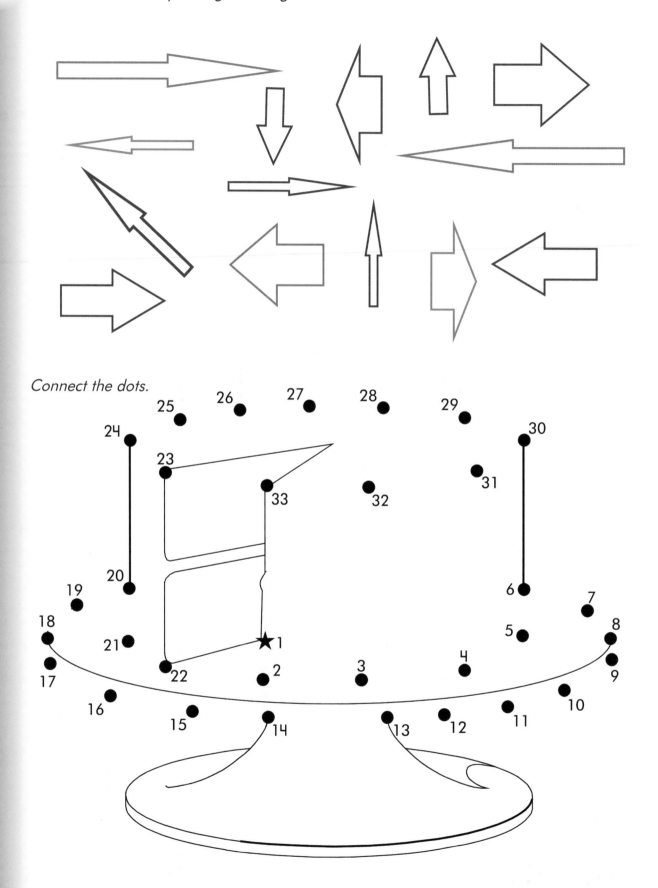

Count by ones.

20 ___ ___ ___ 24 ___ ___ 27 ___ 29

___ 31 ___ ___ 34 ___ 36 ___ 38 ___ 40

Cross out the shapes that are not a square.

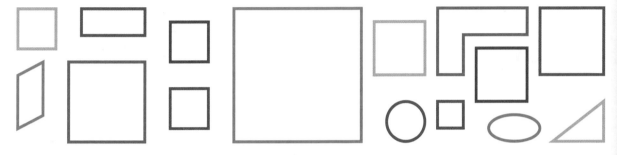

Write the vowel sound you hear in the picture.

___
- - - - -

___
- - - -

___
- - - - -

Put an X on the pictures that do not end with the /g/ sound.

12

Which picture does not belong with the others? Why?

Wednesday

Add.

5	9	2	1	0	1	2	1	6
+0	+1	+2	+3	+4	+6	+7	+8	+1

Write in the number that comes before and after (counting by ones).

_____ 10 _____   _____ 13 _____   _____ 16 _____

_____ 12 _____   _____ 18 _____   _____ 17 _____

_____ 14 _____   _____ 11 _____   _____ 15 _____

Circle the letter that is the same as the first letter in each row.

i	y	i	y
x	w	w	x
t	t	l	l

d	b	b	d
o	o	c	c
m	n	m	n

e	e	a	a
h	r	h	r
j	g	g	j

Match the sentence and the picture.

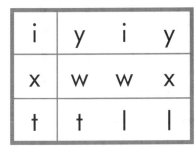

 Dad drives a truck.

The pot is big and fat.

 Ann has a quilt.

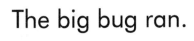 The big bug ran.

13

Use the numbers to color the picture.

1 - red   4 - green   6 - purple

2 - yellow   5 - orange   7 - brown

3 - blue

Thursday

Count by tens.

10 _____ _____ 40 _____ _____ 70 _____ 90 _____

_____ 20 _____ _____ 50 _____ _____ 80 _____ 100

Write what comes next on the line.

♡✖❀♡✖❀ _____   OOOOOO _____

▲▼▲▼ _____   yzyzyz _____

□▫□□▫□ _____   ☒☑☒☑ _____

Select a letter to make a word.

ho _____   ye _____   du _____
   p b   j s   s g

li _____   fa _____   po _____
   t r   v n   t n

Circle the pictures that have the short /e/ sound in the middle of the word.

14

Draw a line from each picture to the sentence that describes it.

Pam had a big bed.

Tim got a red van.

Is a hat in the box?

Jim did get a jet.

Help each animal get to the barn.

Add.

0+3= _____   2+4= _____   5+2= _____

1+6= _____   4+0= _____   0+5= _____

3+5= _____   6+0= _____   1+4= _____

Match the numbers that are the same.

46	97
35	46
97	64
64	35

22	11
12	22
11	12
21	21

78	80
52	46
80	52
46	78

Draw a picture of the sentence.

The cat is in the box.	A leaf is on the grass.

Put an X on the pictures that do not begin with the /v/ sound.

15

Cut out the shapes and arrange them to form the picture. For extra fun you may glue the shapes to another piece of paper.

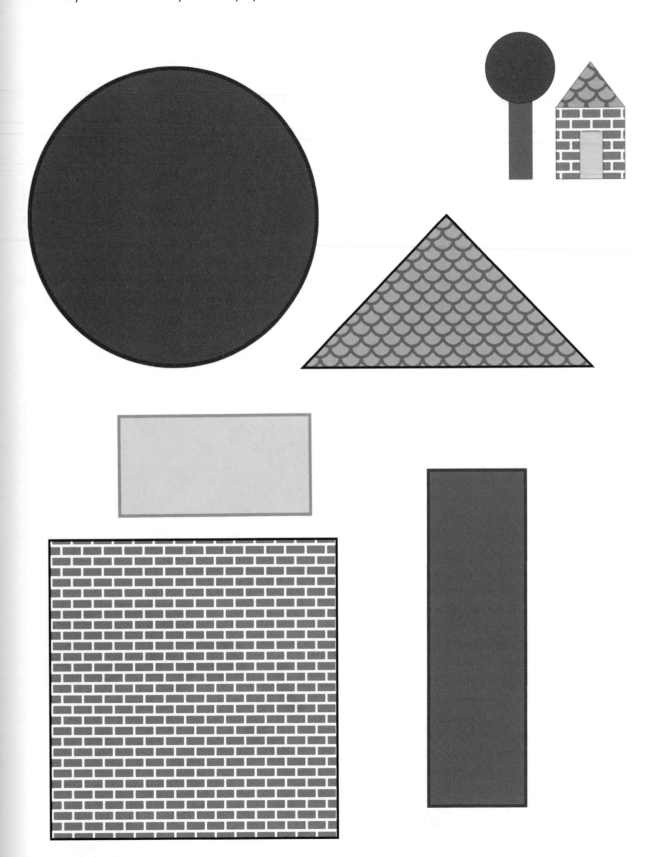

Add.

1	3	8	0	2	5	7	3	6
+0	+5	+2	+7	+8	+4	+0	+1	+3

Count the objects.

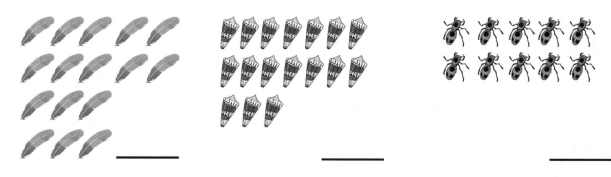

_____   _____   _____

Circle the word that is different in each row.

made	make	make
load	load	road
meat	meet	meat

dim	dime	dim
tune	tone	tone
take	take	tape

Circle the pictures that end with the /m/ sound.

Draw a line from each picture to the sentence that describes it.

Is an ant big?

An elk is big.

Ann can huff and puff.

Bob and Kim had fun.

Connect the dots.

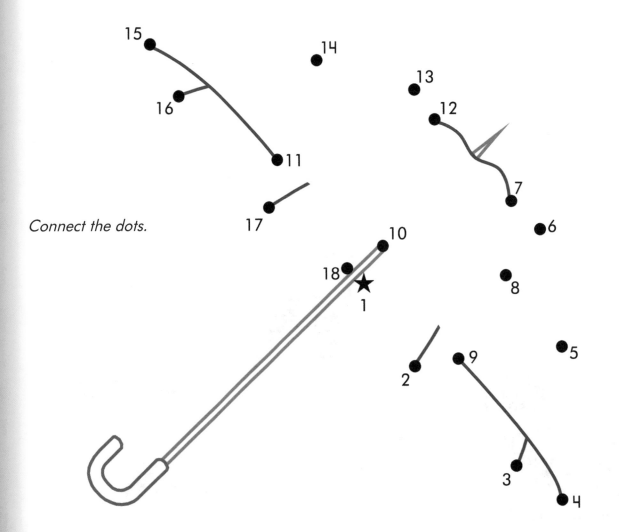

Count by fives.

50 _____ 60 _____ 70 75 _____ 85 _____ 95 _____

50 55 _____ _____ 70 75 _____ 85 90 _____ _____

Circle the rectangles.

Number the days of the week in order.

____ Friday   ____ Monday   ____ Thursday

____ Sunday   ____ Wednesday   ____ Saturday

____ Tuesday

Circle the pictures beginning with the /j/ sound.

17

Circle the sentence that finishes each story.

1. Dan had a big bin.
2. Dan set ten men in the bin.
3. Dan set six jets in the bin.

4. Dan had lots and lots in the bin.

or

4. Dan had a nap in the bin.

1. Mom got a pot.
2. Mom set a ham in the pot.
3. The pot got hot.

4. The pot is a cat.

or

4. The ham got hot.

1. Meg has a pet.
2. Meg's pet is not big.
3. Meg fed the pet bits.

4. Meg and the pet had fun.

or

4. The pet is a big fox.

Wednesday

Add.

0+0= _____   3+2= _____   1+4= _____

2+5= _____   5+5= _____   6+0= _____

0+9= _____   4+2= _____   3+7= _____

Write the number that comes before and after (counting by ones).

_____ 25 _____   _____ 39 _____   _____ 35 _____

_____ 21 _____   _____ 31 _____   _____ 37 _____

_____ 28 _____   _____ 22 _____   _____ 33 _____

Write the word on the lines under the correct picture.

tack   map   bus

_____   _____   _____

Number the sentences in the order they happened.

_____ Sam went to bed.   _____ The bug ate and ate.

_____ Sam ate his meal.   _____ The bug is not big.

_____ Sam had fun in the   _____ The bug is big.
grass.

18

Circle the animals that have feathers.

Thursday

Count by ones.

81 ___ ___ 84 ___ ___ 87 ___ 89 ___

91 ___ ___ 94 ___ ___ 97 ___ 99 ___

Circle the smallest number in each row.

22	42	90
55	33	71
89	20	44

55	17	94
81	66	57
92	85	77

Choose one of the letters and write in on the line to make a word.

b ___ d   j ___ g   r ___ t
  e i   e u   o i

c ___ p   l ___ d   s ___ n
  u e   i o   i a

Circle the pictures that begin with the /t/ sound.

19

Circle the object that should come next.

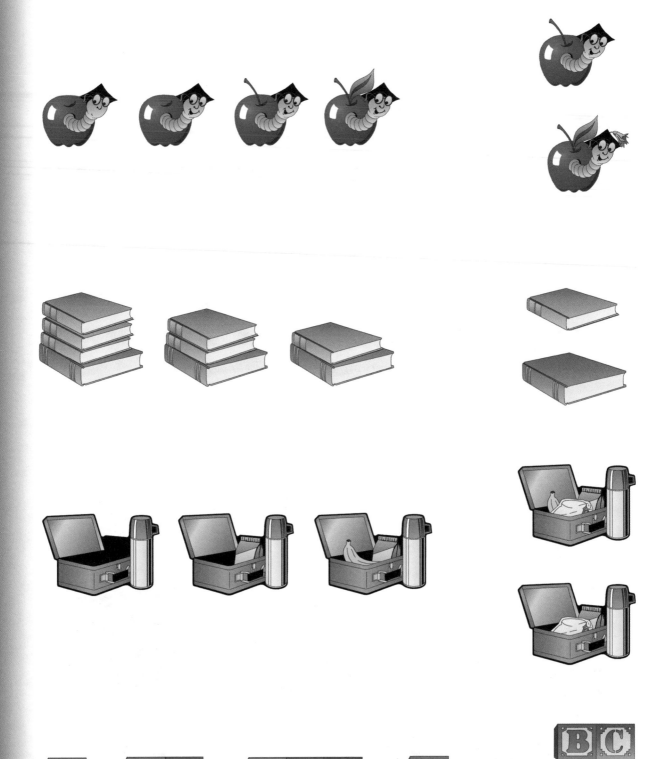

Add.

4	6	3	2	1	4	0	6	3
+6	+3	+0	+3	+6	+1	+5	+1	+4

Draw a line to "cut" each shape in half.

Write the lowercase letter next to the capital.

D _____   P _____   B _____

N _____   Z _____   L _____

X _____   J _____   V _____

Put an X on the pictures that do not end with the /f/ sound.

20

Color the loud things red. Color the quiet things blue.

Add.

9+0= _____   3+6= _____   0+7= _____

1+0= _____   3+2= _____   1+8= _____

5+4= _____   2+7= _____   0+1= _____

Color the correct number of objects.

14 ○ ○ ○ ○ ○ ○ ○ ○ ○ ○ ○ ○ ○ ○ ○ ○

19 ✦

17 | | | | | | | | | | | | | | | | | | | | | | | | | | | | | | | |

Write the letter for the first sound in the picture.

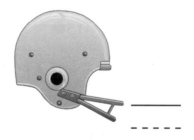

_____   _____   _____

- - - -   - - - -   - - - -

_____   _____   _____

Circle the pictures that begin with the /c/ or /k/ sound.

21

Draw a line to connect the letters in order.

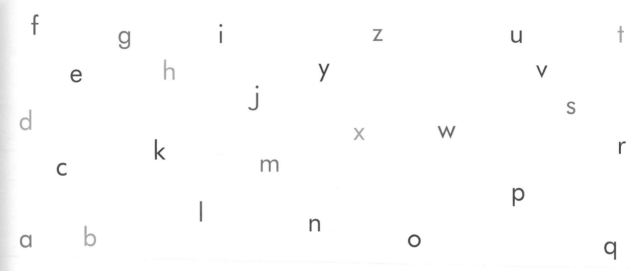

f   g   i   z   u   t

e   h   y   v

j   s

d   x   w   r

k

c   m   p

l   n

a   b   o   q

Connect the dots.

Tuesday

Count by ones.

40 ____ ____ 43 ____ 45 ____ ____ ____ 49

____ 51 ____ 53 54 ____ ____ 57 58 ____ 60

Color the largest circle in each box.

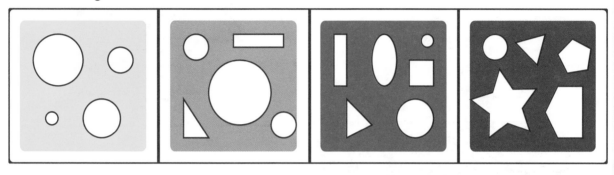

Circle the two words in each row that rhyme.

fan	fun	pan
hid	hip	lip
cup	pup	pop

bed	red	rod
job	rod	rob
fix	fox	box

Put an X on the pictures that do not end with the /d/ sound.

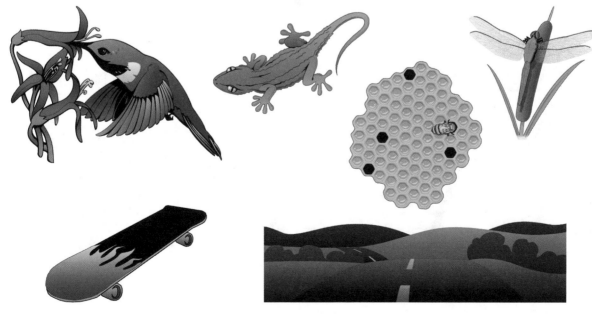

22

Which picture does not belong with the other?   Why?

Wednesday

Add.

$$
\begin{array}{cccccccc}
3 & 4 & 0 & 1 & 4 & 7 & 2 & 8 & 3 \\
+0 & +1 & +9 & +1 & +3 & +0 & +5 & +2 & +6 \\
\end{array}
$$

Write the number that comes before and after (counting by ones).

____ 19 ____   ____ 5 ____   ____ 2 ____

____ 20 ____   ____ 7 ____   ____ 6 ____

____ 13 ____   ____ 8 ____   ____ 4 ____

Circle the word that is the same as the first word in the row.

fine	fin	fine	file
rake	rake	make	rack
goat	boat	got	goat

mule	mule	mute	yule
hike	bike	hide	hike
bean	been	bean	dean

Match the word and the picture.

dog

pan

tree

vote

Help the drummer find his way to the parade.

Color the picture. The numbers tell you what color to use.

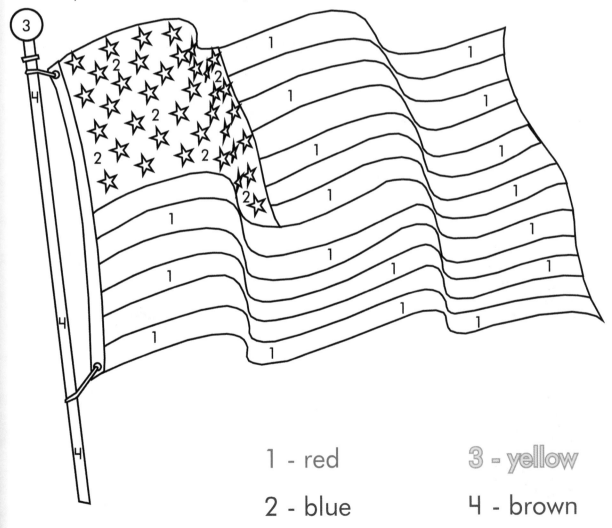

1 - red   3 - yellow

2 - blue   4 - brown

Thursday

Count by tens.

10 _____ _____ 40 50 _____ _____ _____ 90 100

_____ 20 _____ _____ 50 _____ _____ 80 _____ 100

Write what comes next on the line.

↘↗↘↗ _____ mnmnmn _____

6 9 6 9 _____ 133133_____

●■▲◇●■▲◇ _____ ##○##○ _____

Draw a picture of the word in the box.

hat	bug	leg

Circle the pictures that have the short /i/ sound in the middle of the word.

24

Circle the sentence that tells about the picture.

The map is big.

The van is big.

Hal had a box.

Hal had a bag.

The mud is wet.

The sun is hot.

The rat is a bed.

The rat is big.

Help the man get to work.

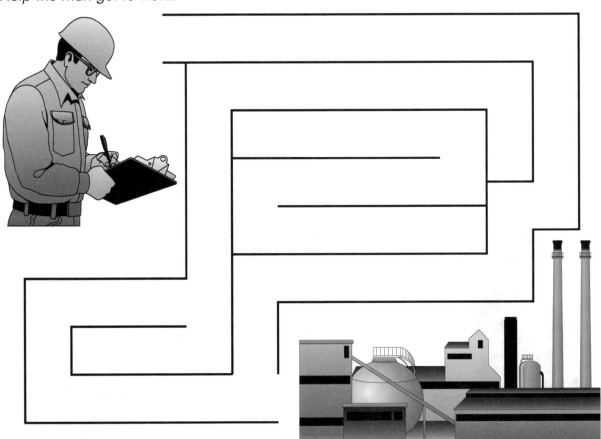

Add.

8+0= _____   4+4= _____   6+2= _____

2+6= _____   0+8= _____   3+3= _____

5+1= _____   9+0= _____   1+2= _____

Put an X on the number that is different in each row.

57	57	75	57
82	28	82	82
43	43	33	43

66	66	66	99
21	12	12	12
19	91	19	19

Match the upper and lower case letters.

C	o
O	a
A	c

K	y
Y	k
M	m

W	u
I	i
U	w

Put an X on the pictures that do not begin with the /r/ sound.

25

Use the numbers to color the picture.

1 - red   4 - green   6 - purple

2 - yellow   5 - orange   7 - brown

3 - blue

Add.

2	3	1	8	4	0	7	4	5
+3	+6	+5	+0	+5	+2	+2	+3	+2

Draw the correct number of suns in each box.

8	5	10

In each row, circle the letter that is different.

a	a	a	o	a
f	t	f	f	f
k	h	h	h	

u	u	u	n
e	e	c	e
r	m	r	r

p	q	q	q
v	v	v	w
d	d	b	d

Circle the pictures that have the /x/ sound at the end.

26

Match the shapes that are alike.

Connect the dots.

Count by fives.

5 ____ ____ 20 ____ 30 ____ ____ ____ 50

____ 10 ____ 20 25 ____ ____ 40 ____ ____

Color the largest square in each box.

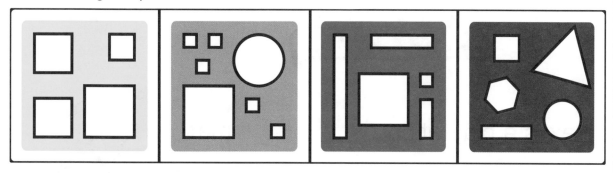

Write the capital letter next to the lowercase letter.

____ e   ____ q   ____ c

____ o   ____ a   ____ m

____ y   ____ k   ____ w

Circle the pictures that begin with the /l/ sound.

27

Read each rhyme and circle the word that should fill in the blank.

Jen is not a big tot.   hug

Jen sat on the _____.   cot

Rex is a big, fat cat.   mat

Rex had a nap on a _____.   fox

Ben got a tan rag.   bag

Ben set the rag in a _____.   hot

Ken met Ted and Wes.   Tim

Jon met Ron and _____.   Les

Wednesday

Add.

0+5= _____   1+7= _____   2+1= _____

4+0= _____   3+4= _____   5+3= _____

1+9= _____   7+3= _____   8+1= _____

Write the number that comes before and after (counting by ones).

_____ 36 _____   _____ 29 _____   _____ 20 _____

_____ 32 _____   _____ 24 _____   _____ 23 _____

_____ 40 _____   _____ 21 _____   _____ 26 _____

Draw a picture of the phrase.

a blue bus	a glad mom	six flags

Match the rhyming pictures.

28

Fill in the missing numbers.

1	2	3	4	5	6	7		9	10
11	12	13		15	16	17	18	19	20
21	22	23	24		26	27	28	29	30
31	32	33	34	35	36	37	38	39	
41	42		44	45	46	47	48	49	50
51		53	54	55	56	57	58	59	60
61	62	63	64	65		67	68	69	70
	72	73	74	75	76	77	78	79	80
81	82	83	84	85	86		88	89	90
91	92	93	94	95	96	97	98		100

Thursday

Count by ones.

1 _____ _____ 4 _____ _____ _____ 8 _____ _____

_____ 12 _____ _____ 15 _____ 17 _____ _____ 20

Write a larger number on the line.

47 _____   32 _____   89 _____

2 _____   14 _____   70 _____

25 _____   91 _____   64 _____

Write the letter for the last sound of the picture.

_____

- - - - -

_____

- - - - -

_____

- - - - -

Circle the pictures that begin with the /g/ sound.

29

Circle the object that should come next.

Add.

4	0	5	2	8	0	1	2	5
+ 5	+ 2	+ 2	+ 7	+ 1	+ 3	+ 8	+ 1	+ 5

Circle the shapes that have been divided in half.

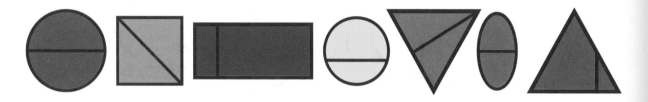

Choose one of the letters and write it on the line to make a word.

_____ an	_____ og	_____ ill
p g	n l	h z

_____ un	_____ ed	_____ at
f m	k b	w m

Circle the pictures that end with a /b/ sound.

30

Color the hot things orange. Color the cold things purple.

Add.

$0+1=$ _____ $1+2=$ _____ $7+2=$ _____

$2+4=$ _____ $5+3=$ _____ $1+9=$ _____

$6+2=$ _____ $3+3=$ _____ $7+3=$ _____

Count the objects.

 _____   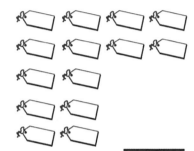 _____    _____

Circle the correct word.

crab   crabs   clip   clips   rat   rats

Put an X on the pictures that do not begin with the /p/ sound.

Connect the dots.

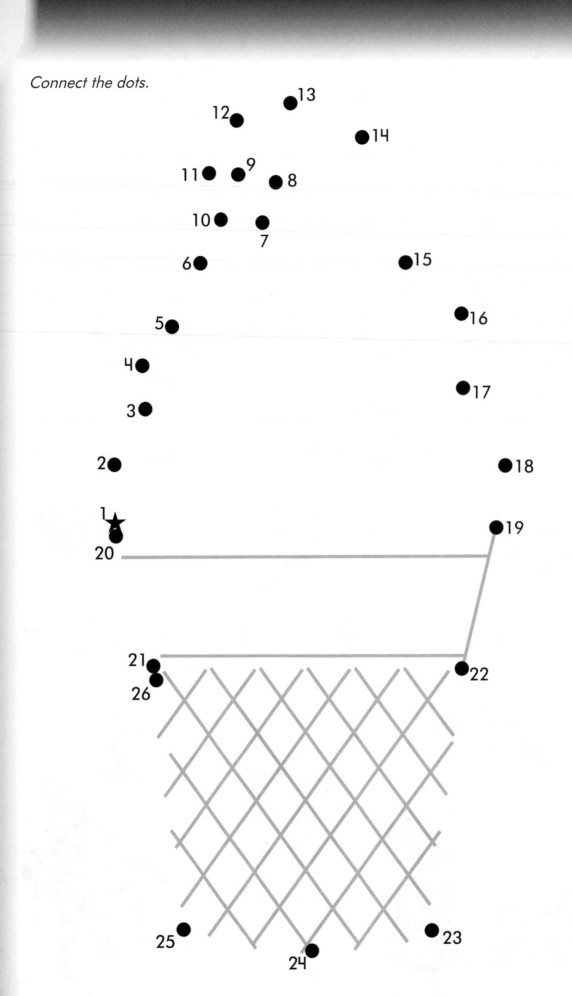

Count by ones.

1 _____ _____ 4 _____ _____ 7 _____ _____ 10 _____

12 _____ _____ 15 _____ _____ 18 _____ _____

Put an X on the largest rectangle in each box.

Write the vowel sound you hear in the picture.

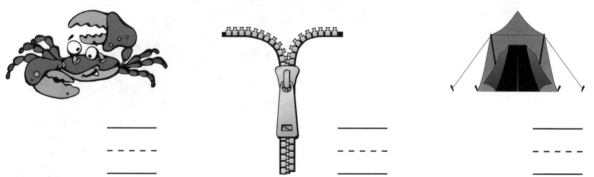

_____   _____   _____

- - - - -   - - - - -   - - - - -

Circle the pictures that end with the /v/ sound.

32

Which picture does not belong with the others? Why?

Wednesday

Add.

6	2	7	8	4	0	3	2	5
+2	+0	+3	+1	+5	+3	+1	+7	+2

What comes before and after the number (counting by ones)?

____ 7 ____   ____ 3 ____   ____ 17 ____

____ 1 ____   ____ 9 ____   ____ 12 ____

____ 11 ____   ____ 3 ____   ____ 19 ____

Circle the letter that is the same as the first letter in each row.

y	p	y	p
h	r	r	h
j	j	g	g

n	m	m	n
u	u	n	n
z	k	z	k

c	c	o	o
q	a	a	q
l	t	l	t

Match the sentence and the picture.

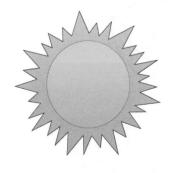

The ram is big.

Dad's hat is tan.

The meat is red.

The sun is hot.

33

Use the numbers to color the picture.

1 - red   4 - green   6 - purple

2 - yellow   5 - orange   7 - brown

3 - blue

Thursday

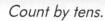

Count by tens.

10 _____ 30 _____ _____ 60 _____ _____ 90 _____

_____ _____ _____ 40 50 60 _____ _____ _____ 100

Write what comes next on the line.

468468 _____   pqpqpq _____

✔✱✔✱ _____   ➡▷▷➡▷▷ _____

▷▷▷▷ _____   ♪♫♪♫ _____

Select a letter to make a word.

ba _____   go _____   me _____
      q d   t c   b t

nu _____   si _____   va _____
      r t   g p   n v

Put an X on the pictures that do not begin with the /f/ sound.

34

Draw a line from each picture to the sentence that describes it.

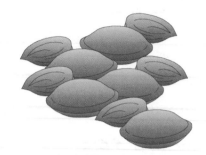

Nan got six pods.

Hal got ten nuts.

The bun is a big bun.

The mug is hot.

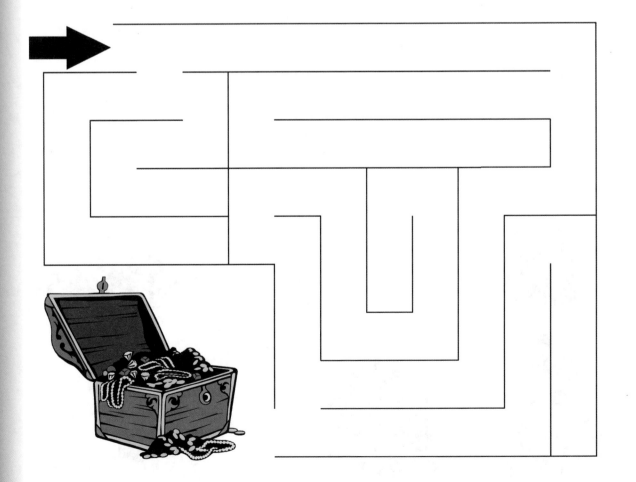

Add.

0+5= _____   7+2= _____   9+0= _____

3+3= _____   4+1= _____   6+3= _____

9+1= _____   2+1= _____   2+7= _____

Circle the numbers that are the same as the first number in the row.

34	34	44	34	33
95	59	95	99	95
69	66	69	69	96

77	17	77	77	71
56	65	56	66	56
85	85	58	88	85

Draw a picture of the sentence.

A ham is in the pan.	The goat can eat.

Circle the pictures that have the short /o/ sound in the middle of the word.

35

Cut out the shapes and arrange them to form the picture. For extra fun, glue the shapes to another piece of paper and hang up your finished picture.

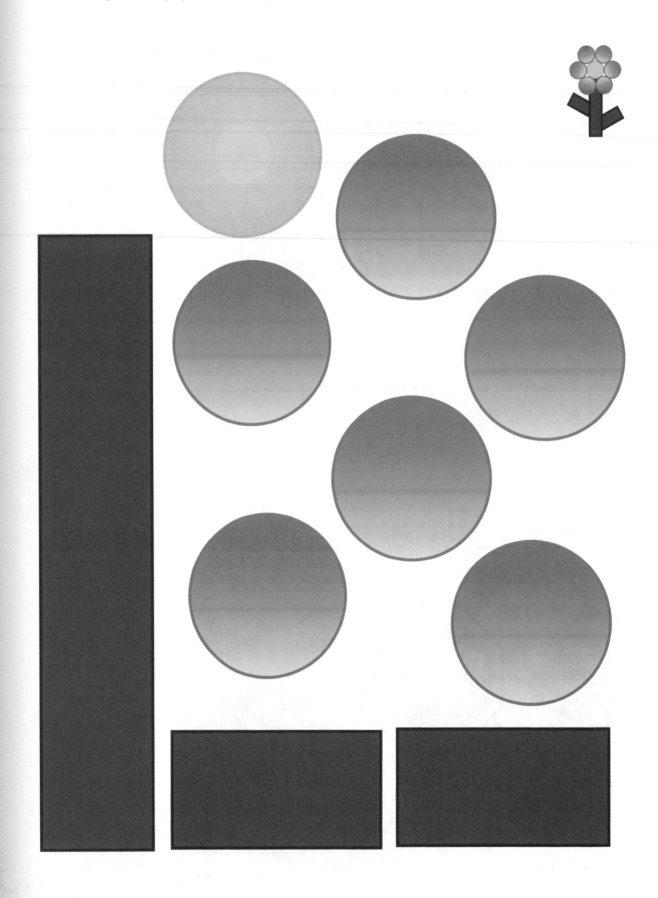

Monday

Add.

8	5	1	5	2	7	4	3	1
+0	+1	+0	+5	+3	+1	+2	+6	+4

Color the correct number of objects.

18 0 0 0 0 0 0 0 0 0 0 0 0 0 0 0 0 0 0 0 0 0 0

15 ✏✏✏✏✏✏✏✏✏✏✏✏✏✏✏✏✏✏

13 📖📖📖📖📖📖📖📖📖📖📖📖📖📖📖📖📖📖

Circle the word that is different in each row.

wig	wag	wig	wig
mad	mad	sad	mad
fell	felt	felt	felt

stop	stop	stop	step
bag	beg	beg	beg
sun	fun	sun	sun

Put an X on the pictures that do not have the /i/ sound at the beginning.

36

Connect the dots.

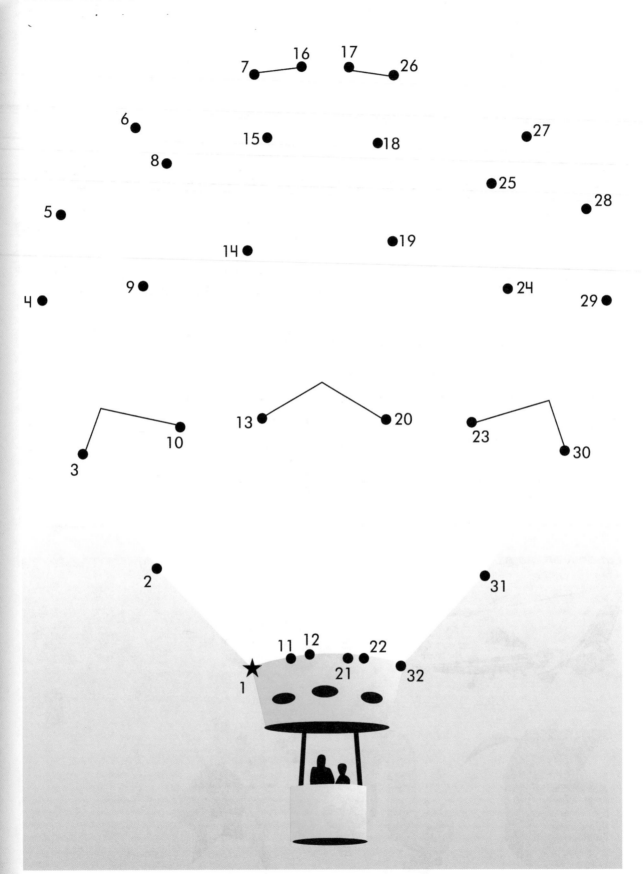

Count by fives.

5 _____ _____ 20 _____ _____ 35 _____ _____ 50

_____ 60 _____ _____ 75 _____ _____ 90 95 _____

Color the smallest triangle in each box.

Number the days of the week in order.

____ Sunday   ____ Thursday   ____ Saturday

____ Wednesday   ____ Monday   ____ Tuesday

                     ____ Friday

Circle the pictures that begin with the short /a/ sound.

37

Circle the sentence that finishes each story.

1. Max is Kim's pet.
2. Max can run and sit.
3. Max can beg.

4. Max is a fun pet.

    or

4. Max is a big cat.

1. Jen's top had a rip.
2. Can Mom fix the rip?
3. Mom got Jen's top.

4. The rip is a leg.

    or

4. Mom did fix the rip in Jen's top.

1. Mom had a tot.
2. The tot is Ben.
3. The tot can sip and sip.

4. Ben can sip and sip.

    or

4. Ben is hot and sad.

Wednesday

Add.

7+2= _____   5+0= _____   3+3= _____

1+7= _____   6+3= _____   4+1= _____

2+2= _____   0+2= _____   3+0= _____

Write the number that comes before and after (counting by ones).

_____ 33 _____   _____ 32 _____   _____ 37 _____

_____ 27 _____   _____ 39 _____   _____ 29 _____

_____ 36 _____   _____ 34 _____   _____ 28 _____

Write the word on the line under the correct picture.

tent   **hen**   **pig**

_____   _____   _____
- - - - - - - - -   - - - - - - - - -   - - - - - - - - -
_____   _____   _____

Number the sentences in the order they happened.

_____ The plant is big.   _____ A cat came.

_____ See Jill plant the   _____ The rat ran and
        seed.   ran.

_____ The rain fell on   _____ A rat sat on a
        the seed.   mat.

38

Circle the animals that live in water.

Thursday

Count by ones.

61 _____ 63 _____ _____ _____ _____ 68 _____ 70

71 _____ _____ _____ 75 76 _____ _____ 79 _____

Circle the smallest number in each row.

46	18	59
35	47	27
41	83	26

52	91	60
76	14	38
82	30	25

Choose one of the letters and write it on the line to make a word.

d _____ g
  e o

k _____ d
  i a

t _____ p
  o e

f _____ n
  u o

m _____ p
  e o

v _____ n
  i a

Put an X on the pictures that do not begin with the /d/ sound.

Draw a line to the object that should come next.

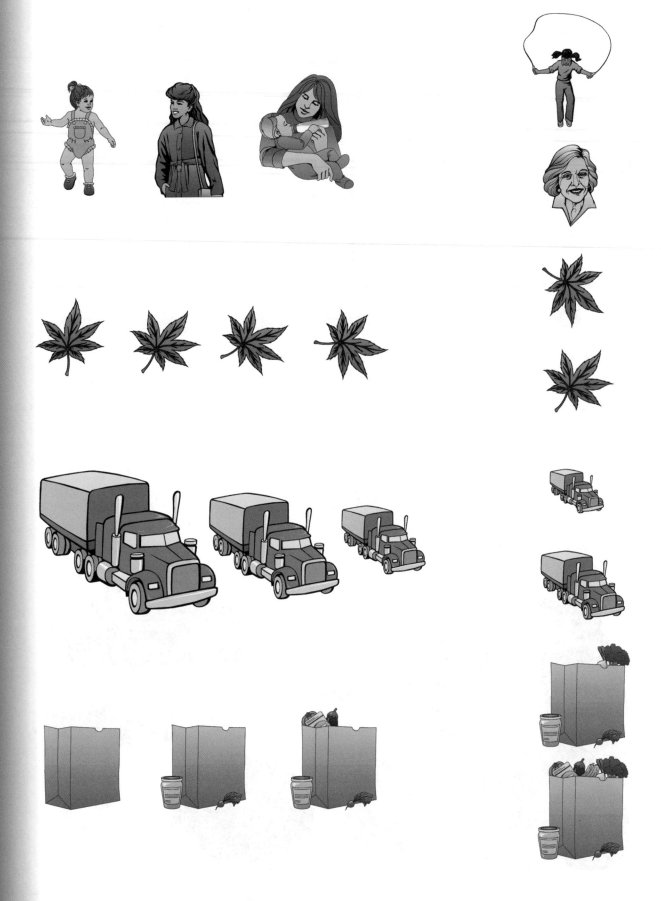

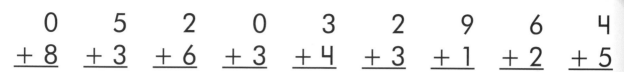

Add.

```
  0     5     2     0     3     2     9     6     4
+ 8   + 3   + 6   + 3   + 4   + 3   + 1   + 2   + 5
```

Color one half of each shape.

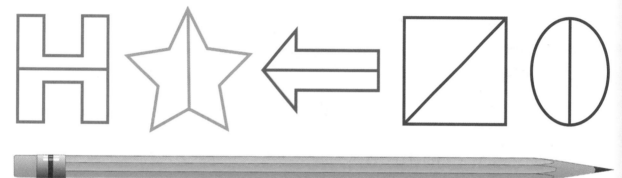

Write the capital letter next to the lowercase letter.

_____ h   _____ t   _____ f

_____ r   _____ d   _____ p

_____ b   _____ n   _____ z

Circle the pictures that end with the /t/ sound.

40

Circle the sentence that tells about the picture.

It has red on it.

It has tan on it.

The ant got it.

The ox got it.

The rat bit it.

The cat can hit it.

It is hot and wet.

It can pop up at a tot.

Help the ship find its way to land.

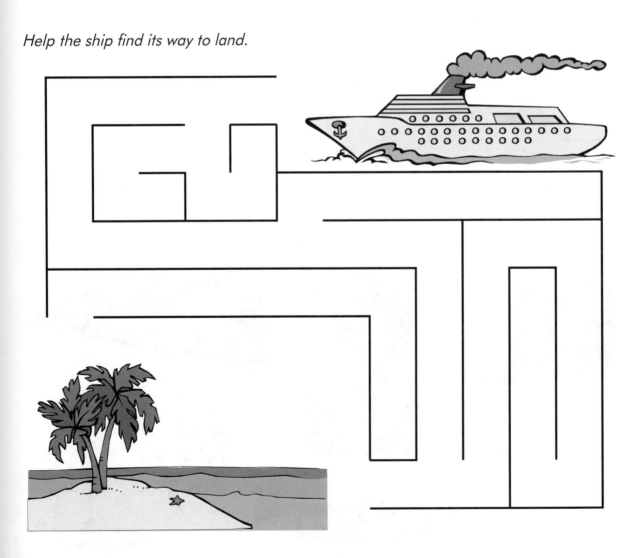

Add.

1+3= _____   2+6= _____   4+2= _____

3+7= _____   1+7= _____   3+1= _____

2+0= _____   0+8= _____   1+5= _____

Draw the correct number of squares.

7	6	10

Write the letter for the first sound in the picture.

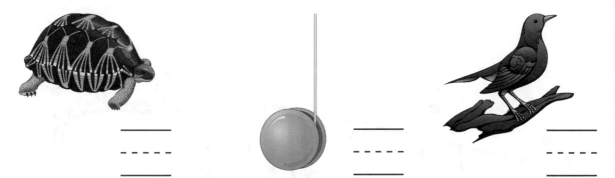

_ _ _ _ _   _ _ _ _ _   _ _ _ _ _

Put an X on the pictures that do not start with the /m/ sound.

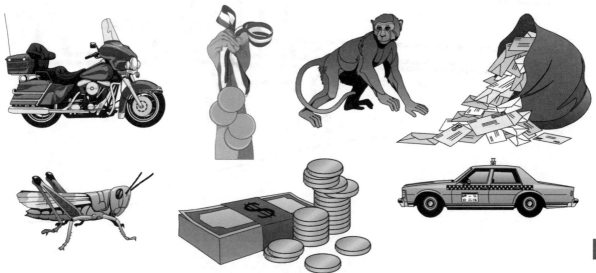

41

Color all the arrows pointing to the left.

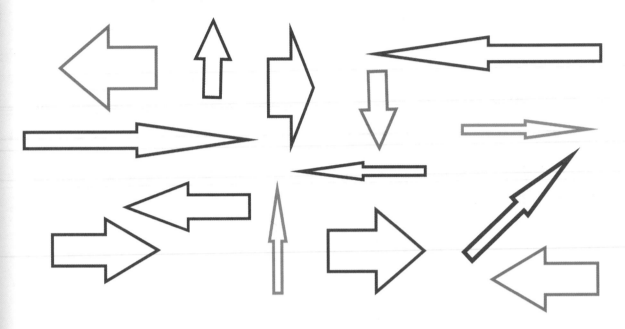

Connect the dots.

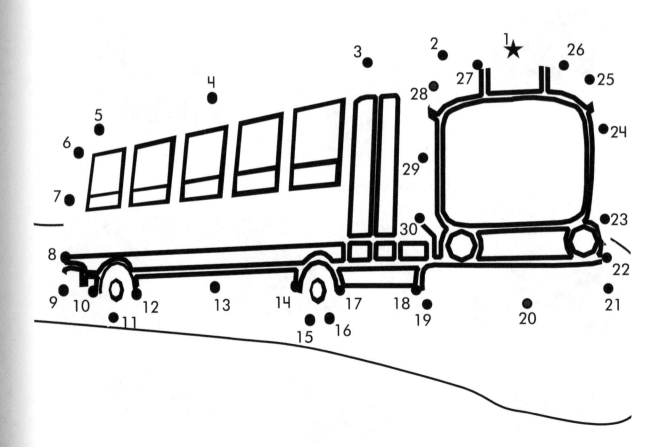

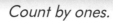

Count by ones.

20 ____ ____ ____ 24 ____ ____ ____ 28 ____

30 ____ ____ 33 34 ____ ____ 37 ____ ____ 40

In each box, put an X on the shape that does not belong.

Match the rhyming words.

sun	win
pin	cot
hot	fun

ten	tell
had	men
bell	lad

Circle the pictures that end with the /s/ sound.

42

Which picture does not belong with the others? Why?

Wednesday

Add.

1	5	3	0	1	0	6	8	2
+0	+4	+2	+5	+9	+4	+1	+2	+4

What comes before and after the number?

____ 8 ____   ____ 13 ____   ____ 14 ____

____ 2 ____   ____ 12 ____   ____ 16 ____

____ 5 ____   ____ 10 ____   ____ 20 ____

Circle the word that is the same as the first word in the row.

pen	pen	pin	pet
hit	hat	hit	hot
sad	sat	sag	sad

top	tap	mop	top
get	get	got	jet
mud	bud	mud	mad

Match the word and the picture.

cake

hot dog

jet

mule

Use the numbers to color the picture.

1 - red   4 - green   6 - purple

2 - yellow   5 - orange   7 - brown

3 - blue

Thursday

Count by tens.

10 _____ 30 _____ _____ _____ _____ 80 _____ 100

_____ _____ _____ 40 _____ 60 _____ 80 _____ 100

Draw what comes next on the line.

 _____   88888 _____

 _____   rstrst _____

 _____   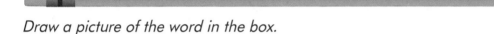 _____

Draw a picture of the word in the box.

bun	dog	cake

Put an X on the pictures that do not have the short /u/ sound in the middle of the word.

44

Color the wiggly or fast things yellow. Color the still or slow things brown.

Add.

3+0= _____   4+4= _____   0+2= _____

6+1= _____   4+2= _____   2+5= _____

0+7= _____   5+5= _____   1+4= _____

Match the numbers that are the same.

97	37
37	10
10	97
88	88

30	74
61	51
74	30
51	61

42	17
24	42
71	24
17	71

Match the upper and lower case letters.

G	g
S	e
E	s

O	c
C	q
Q	o

A	m
Y	a
M	y

Circle the pictures beginning with the /w/ sound.

45

Connect the dots.

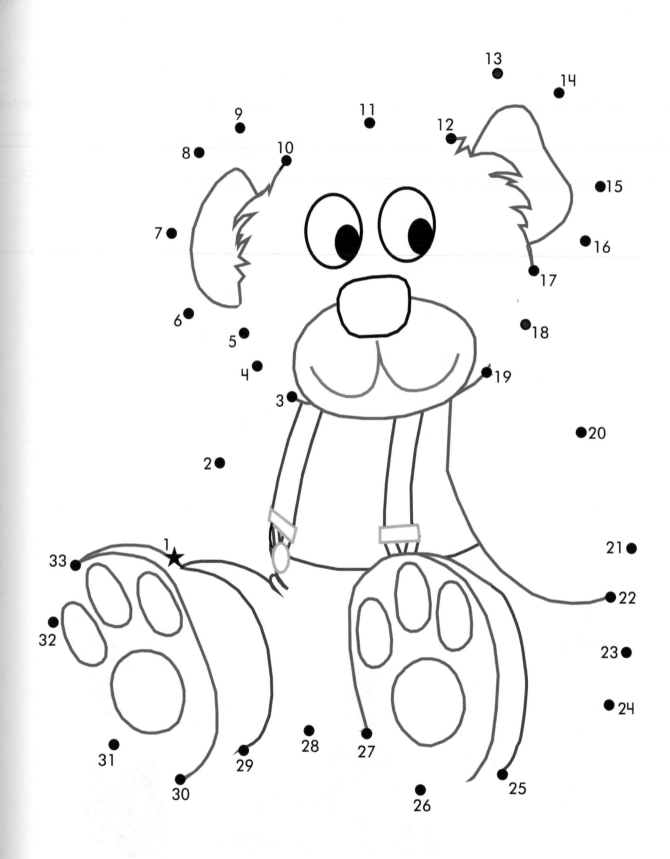

Add.

0	5	2	0	6	3	1	6	1
+0	+3	+1	+7	+4	+4	+2	+0	+8

Count the objects.

 _____

 _____

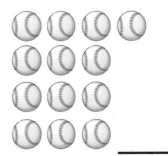 _____

In each row, circle the letter that is different.

z	z	x	z
b	d	d	d
f	f	f	l

l	t	l	l
p	p	q	p
r	n	n	n

v	w	w	w
a	a	a	c
i	j	i	i

Put an X on the pictures that do not have the /n/ sound at the end.

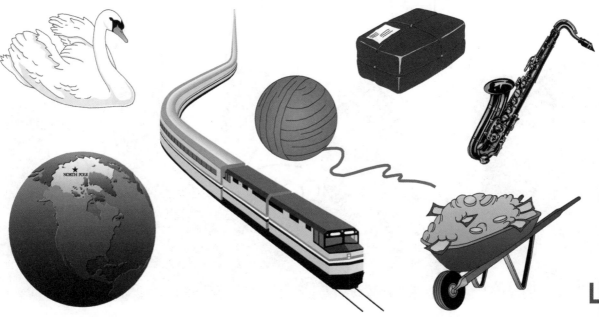

46

Connect the dots.

Tuesday

Count by fives.

50 ___ 60 ___ 70 ___ ___ ___ 90 ___ 100

50 ___ ___ 65 ___ 75 ___ 85 ___ ___ 100

Color the circles red and the rectangles blue.

Write the capital letter next to the lowercase letter.

____ h   ____ t   ____ f

____ r   ____ d   ____ p

____ b   ____ n   ____ z

Circle the pictures that begin with the short /e/ sound.

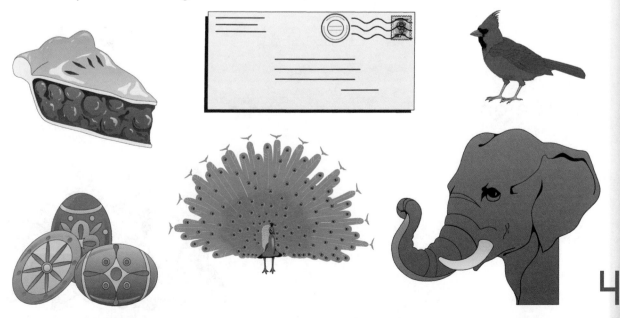

47

Circle the word that completes the rhyme.

Jed is a fat pig.　　　　　　　　　　　hat

Jed had on a big _____.　　wig

Kip is Pam's kid.　　　　　　　　　　lid

Kip can nip a tin _____.　　mat

Mom and Dad's lad is Kit.　　　pen

The lad got a big _____.　　hit

Dad ran and hid.　　　　　　　　　did

Did Rod get him?　　　　　　　　　not

Yes, Rod _____.

Wednesday

Add.

0+6= _____   2+6= _____   0+8= _____

0+9= _____   2+2= _____   5+4= _____

1+6= _____   4+3= _____   8+1= _____

Write the number that comes before and after (counting by ones).

_____ 35 _____   _____ 33 _____   _____ 36 _____

_____ 29 _____   _____ 39 _____   _____ 31 _____

_____ 32 _____   _____ 38 _____   _____ 40 _____

Draw a picture of the phrase.

five green cans	a black bag	a fat pig

Match the rhyming pictures.

48

Fill in the missing numbers.

	2	3	4	5	6	7	8	9	10
11	12	13	14		16	17	18	19	20
21	22	23	24	25	26	27	28		30
31		33	34	35	36	37	38	39	40
41	42	43	44	45	46		48	49	50
51	52	53	54	55	56	57		59	60
61	62	63		65	66	67	68	69	70
71	72	73	74	75		77	78	79	80
81	82		84	85	86	87	88	89	90
91	92	93	94	95	96	97	98	99	

Thursday

Count by ones.

81 ____ 83 ____ ____ ____ ____ 88 ____ 90

____ 92 ____ ____ 95 ____ ____ 98 99 ____

Circle the largest number in each row.

12	16	78
63	37	15
61	11	99

88	48	58
10	72	49
86	95	50

Write the letter for the last sound of the picture.

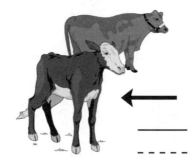

____

- - - - -

____

- - - - -

____

- - - - -

Put an X on the pictures that do not begin with the short /o/ sound.

49

Draw a line to the object that should come next.

Add.

0	1	4	7	5	2	2	0	8
+9	+2	+0	+3	+1	+8	+0	+6	+2

Circle the shapes that have been divided in half.

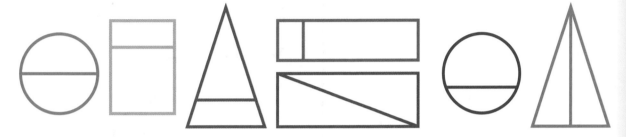

Choose one of the letters and write it on the line to make a word.

_____ eg
l v

_____ ap
t j

_____ ot
s p

_____ up
c w

_____ ib
y b

_____ eck
n z

Circle the pictures that end with the /r/ sound.

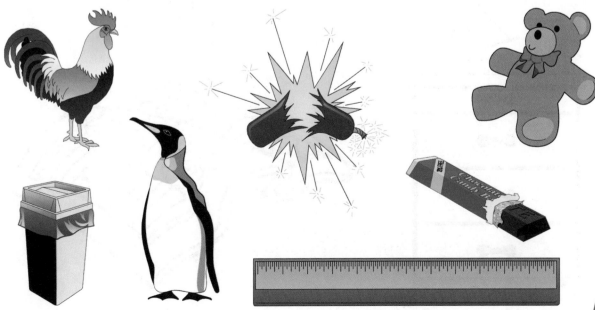

50

Color the hard things green. Color the soft things blue.

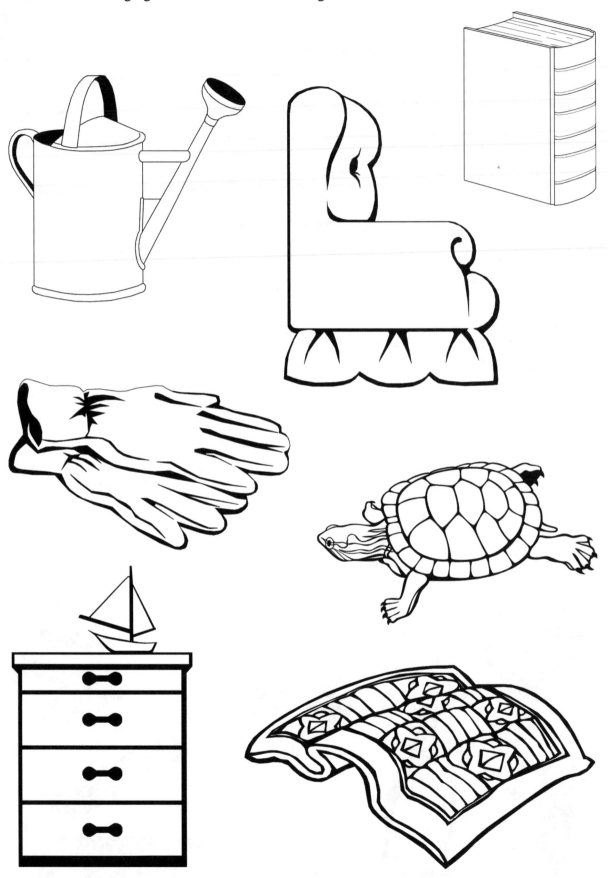

Answer Key

Sometimes there will be more than one right answer to a question. Only one answer is listed in the answer key, but any correct answer should be accepted.

When a child is asked to draw something, make sure he uses the right color, if one is specified.

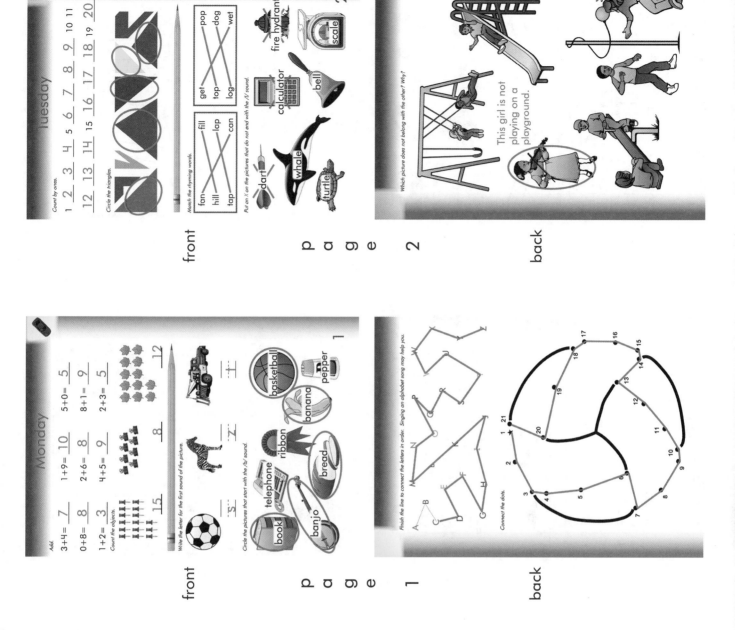

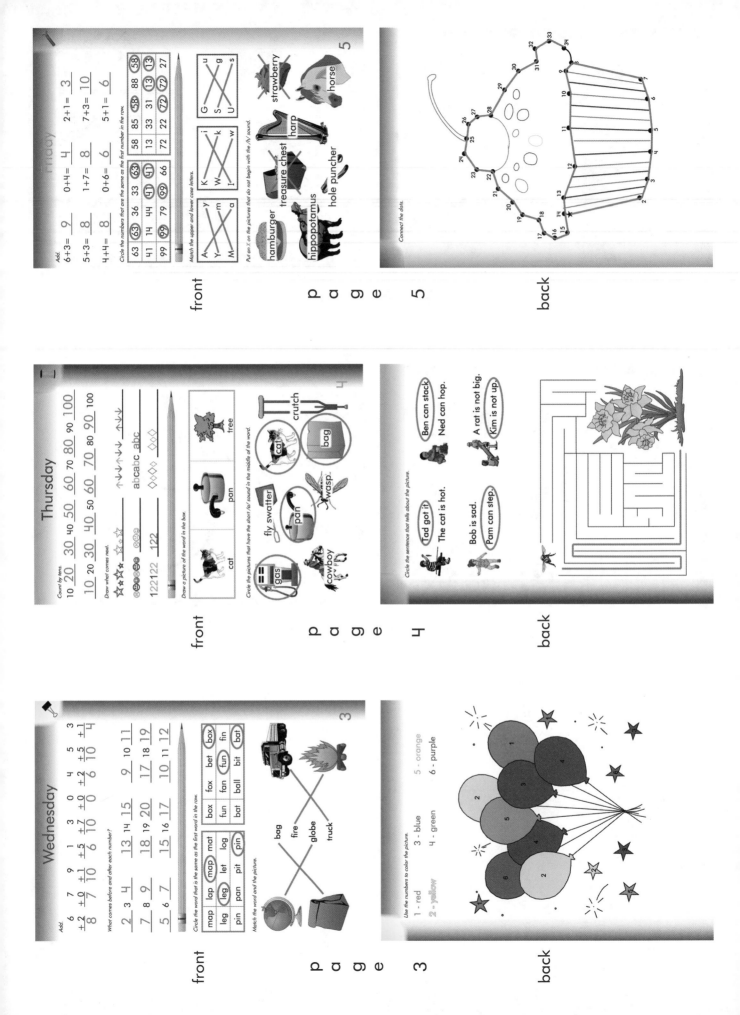

Friday

Add.

6+3= 9	0+4= 4	2+1= 3
5+3= 8	1+7= 8	7+3= 10
4+4= 8	0+6= 6	5+1= 6

Circle the numbers that are the same as the first number in the row.

63	63	36	33
41	41	14	44
99	99	79	66

58	58	58	88
13	13	33	31
72	72	72	27

Match the upper and lower case letters.

K i k w
A y m a
G S U
u g s
Y W I
M

Put an X on the pictures that do not begin with the /h/ sound.

strawberry · horse · harp · treasure chest · hole puncher · hamburger · hippopotamus

front

p a g e 5

Connect the dots.

back

5

Thursday

Count by tens.

10 20 30 40 50 60 70 80 90 100

Draw what comes next.

10 20 30 40 50 60 70 80 90 100

abcabc abc

122122 122

Draw a picture of the word in the box.

cat · pan · tree

Circle the pictures that have the short /a/ sound in the middle of the word.

cat · crutch · bag · wasp · fly swatter · pan · gas · cowboy

front

p a g e 4

Circle the sentence that tells about the picture.

- Ben can stack
- Ned can hop.
- A rat is not big.
- Kim is not up.
- Tad got it
- The cat is hot.
- Bob is sad.
- Pam can step.

back

4

Wednesday

Add.

6 +2 = 8	7 +0 = 7	9 +1 = 10	1 +5 = 6	3 +0 = 3	0 +6 = 6	4 +2 = 6	5 +5 = 10	3 +1 = 4

What comes before and after each number?

2 3 4   13 14 15   9 10 11
7 8 9   18 19 20   17 18 19
5 6 7   15 16 17   10 11 12

Circle the word that is the same as the first word in the row.

map	lap	map	mat
leg	leg	let	log
pin	pin	pit	pin

box	fox	bet	box
fun	fan	fun	fin
bat	ball	bit	bat

Match the word and the picture.

bag · fire · globe · truck

front

p a g e 3

Use the numbers to color the picture.

1 - red   3 - blue   5 - orange
2 - yellow   4 - green   6 - purple

back

3

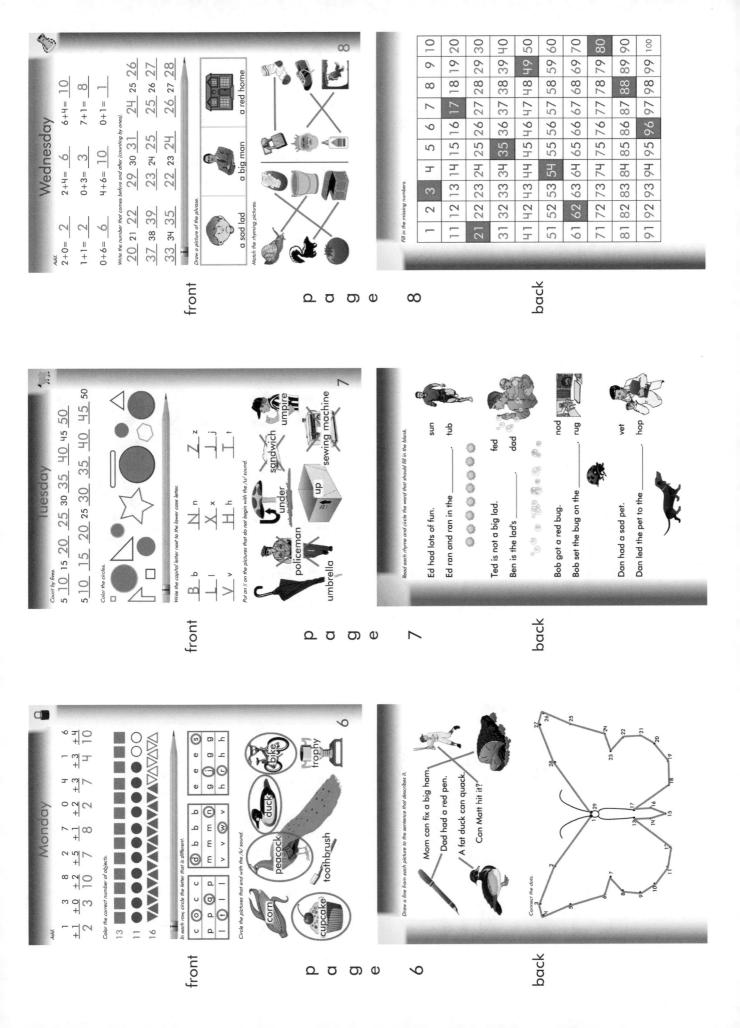

Monday

Add.

1	3	8	2	7	0	4	1	6
+1	+0	+2	+5	+1	+2	+3	+3	+4
2	3	10	7	8	2	7	4	10

Color the correct number of objects.

13
11
16

In each row, circle the letter that is different.

c o c c
d (b) b b
p p (p) t
e e e s
m m (n) m
g (g) g j
v v (w) v
h h (r) h

Circle the pictures that end with the /k/ sound.

corn, peacock, cupcake, duck, bike, trophy, toothbrush

Draw a line from each picture to the sentence that describes it.

Mom can fix a big ham.
Dad had a red pen.
A fat duck can quack.
Can Matt hit it?

Connect the dots.

Tuesday

Count by fives.

5 10 15 20 25 30 35 40 45 50
5 10 15 20 25 30 35 40 45 50

Color the circles.

Write the capital letter next to the lower case letter.

B b   N n   Z z
I i   X x   J j
Y v   H h   I t

Put an X on the pictures that do not begin with the /u/ sound.

umpire, sandwich, sewing machine, under, up, policeman, umbrella

Read each rhyme and circle the word that should fill in the blank.

Ed had lots of fun.   sun
Ed ran and ran in the ___.   tub

Ted is not a big lad.   fed
Ben is the lad's ___.   dad

Bob got a red bug.   nod
Bob set the bug on the ___.   rug

Dan had a sad pet.   vet
Dan led the pet to the ___.   hop

Wednesday

Add.

2+0= 2   2+4= 6   6+4= 10
1+1= 2   0+3= 3   7+1= 8
0+6= 6   4+6= 10   0+1= 1

Write the number that comes before and after (counting by ones).

20 21 22   29 30 31   24 25 26
37 38 39   23 24 25   25 26 27
33 34 35   22 23 24   26 27 28

Draw a picture of the phrase.

a sad lad   a big man   a red home

Match the rhyming pictures.

Fill in the missing numbers.

1	2	3	4	5	6	7	8	9	10
11	12	13	14	15	16	17	18	19	20
21	22	23	24	25	26	27	28	29	30
31	32	33	34	35	36	37	38	39	40
41	42	43	44	45	46	47	48	49	50
51	52	53	54	55	56	57	58	59	60
61	62	63	64	65	66	67	68	69	70
71	72	73	74	75	76	77	78	79	80
81	82	83	84	85	86	87	88	89	90
91	92	93	94	95	96	97	98	99	100

Monday

Add.

3+3= 6	0+9= 9	4+1= 5
4+6= 10	2+0= 2	7+2= 9
2+2= 4	2+8= 10	6+1= 7

Draw the correct number of balls in each box.

7   9   6

Circle the correct word.

grape (grapes)   clock (clocks)   tag (tags)

Circle the pictures that begin with the sound of /n/.

nurse's cap   needle   (nickel)   notebook
newspaper   nose   elephant

front

p a g e 11

Color all the arrows pointing to the right.

Connect the dots.

back

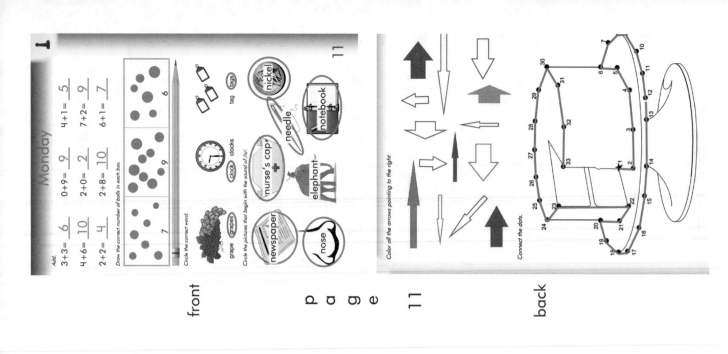

Friday

Add.

6	3	5	0	1	9	2	5	0
+4	+2	+0	+7	+4	+1	+8	+4	+0
10	5	5	7	5	10	10	9	0

Circle the shapes that have been divided in half.

Choose one of the letters and write it on the line to make a word.

s/b ___ix   r/y ___ag   g/q ___um
h/n ___en   j/j ___ob   l/z ___ick

Put an X on the pictures that do not begin with the sound of /s/.

stapler   snow   sandwich   starfish
clown   squirrel   blowing bubbles   key

front

p a g e 10

Circle the pictures of things that happen during the winter.

back

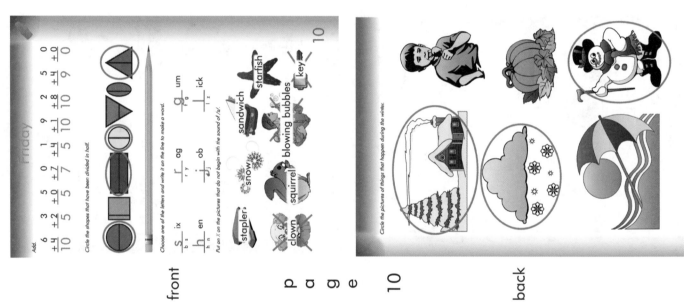

Thursday

Count by ones.

61 62 63 64 65 66 67 68 69 70
71 72 73 74 75 76 77 78 79 80

Circle the largest number in each row.

21	62	(96)
(87)	32	75
28	(75)	...

54	(64)	39
(73)	65	40
53	(84)	76

Write the letter for the last sound of the picture.

___g   ___r   ___g

Circle the pictures that end with the /p/ sound.

lamp   telescope   flowers   mirror   sheep   book   tape

front

p a g e 9

Draw a line to the object that should come next. The first one is done for you.

back

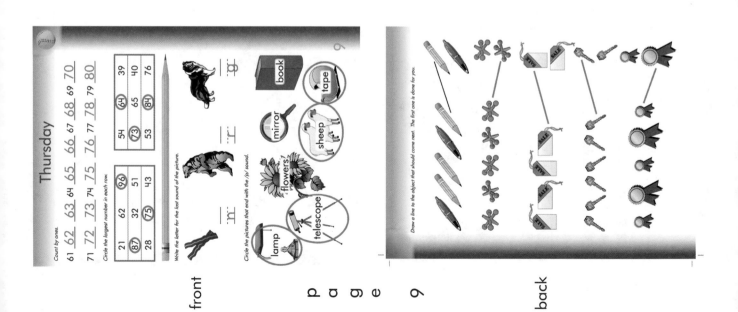

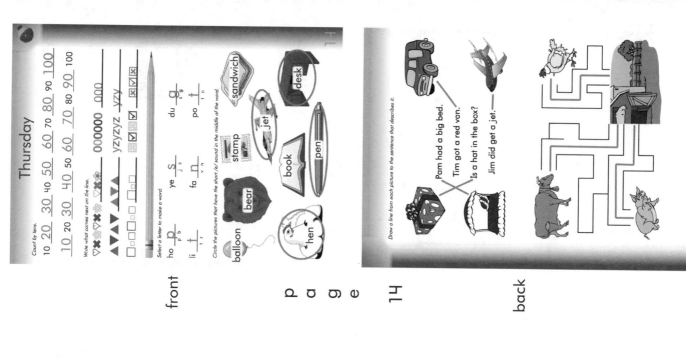

Thursday — front

Count by tens.

10 20 30 40 50 60 70 80 90 100

10 20 30 40 50 60 70 80 90 100

Write what comes next on the line.

×× ⊗∇× ⊗×⊗ _____   000000 _____

▲▼▲ _____

▲▼ ▲▼ ▲▼ _____

□ □ □ □ _____

yzyzyz _____

☑ ☒ ☑ _____

du p/b/g   t/n

Select a letter to make a word.

ho p/b   li t/r   ye s/j   fa n/v   po t/n

Circle the pictures that have the short /e/ sound in the middle of the word.

sandwich   desk   jet   stamp   pen   book   bear   hen   balloon

page 14 — back

Draw a line from each picture to the sentence that describes it.

Pam had a big bed.
Tim got a red van.
Is a hat in the box?
Jim did get a jet.

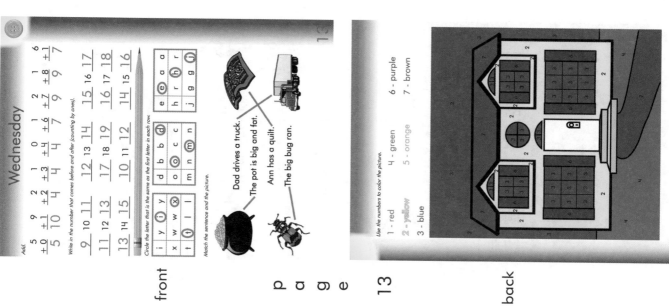

Wednesday — front

Add.

5	9	2	1	0	1	2	1	6
+0	+1	+2	+3	+4	+6	+7	+8	+1
5	10	4	4	4	7	9	9	7

Write in the number that comes before and after (counting by ones).

9 10 11   12 13 14   15 16 17

11 12 13   17 18 19   16 17 18

13 14 15   10 11 12   14 15 16

Circle the letter that is the same as the first letter in each row.

i	y	i	y		d	b	b	d		e	e	a	a
x	w	w	x		o	o	c	c		h	r	h	r
t	l	t	l		m	n	m	n		j	g	g	j

Match the sentence and the picture.

Dad drives a truck.
The pot is big and fat.
Ann has a quilt.
The big bug ran.

page 13 — back

Use the numbers to color the picture.

1 - red   4 - green   6 - purple
2 - yellow   5 - orange   7 - brown
3 - blue

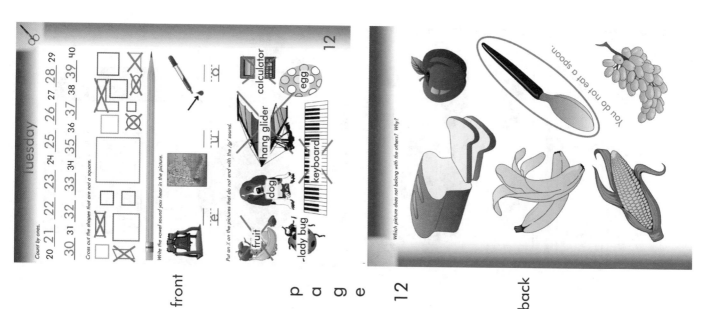

Tuesday — front

Count by ones.

20 21 22 23 24 25 26 27 28 29

30 31 32 33 34 35 36 37 38 39 40

Cross out the shapes that are not a square.

Write the vowel sound you hear in the picture.

_e_   _u_   _o_

Put an X on the pictures that do not end with the /g/ sound.

fruit   lady bug   dog   hang glider   keyboard   calculator   egg

page 12 — back

Which picture does not belong with the others? Why?

You do not eat a spoon.

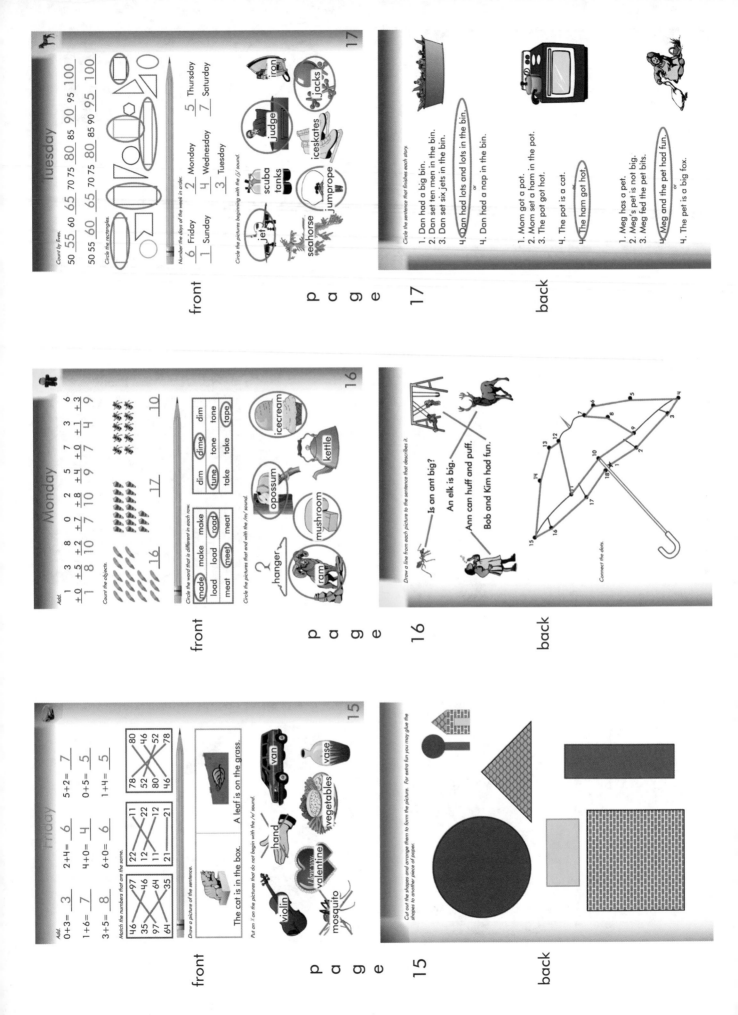

Tuesday — front — page 17

Count by fives.

50 55 60 65 70 75 80 85 90 95 100

50 55 60 65 70 75 80 85 90 95

Circle the rectangles.

Number the days of the week in order.

6 Friday   2 Monday
1 Sunday   4 Wednesday
5 Thursday   3 Tuesday
7 Saturday

Circle the pictures beginning with the /j/ sound.

iron, jacks, judge, iceskates, scuba tanks, jumprope, jet, seahorse

back — page 17

Circle the sentence that finishes each story.

1. Dan had a big bin.
2. Dan set ten men in the bin.
3. Dan set six jets in the bin.
4. Dan had lots and lots in the bin.
or
4. Dan had a nap in the bin.

1. Mom got a pot.
2. Mom set a ham in the pot.
3. The pot got hot.
4. The pot is a cat.
or
4. The ham got hot.

1. Meg has a pet.
2. Meg's pet is not big.
3. Meg fed the pet bits.
4. Meg and the pet had fun.
or
4. The pet is a big fox.

Monday — front — page 16

Add.

1	3	8	0	2	5	7	3	6
+0	+5	+2	+7	+8	+4	+0	+1	+3
1	8	10	7	10	9	7	4	9

Count the objects.

10
17
16

Circle the word that is different in each row.

dim	dime	dim
tune	tone	tone
load	road	load
take	take	tape

Circle the pictures that end with the /m/ sound.

hanger, opossum, icecream, ram, mushroom, kettle

back — page 16

Draw a line from each picture to the sentence that describes it.

Is an ant big?
An elk is big.
Ann can huff and puff.
Bob and Kim had fun.

Connect the dots.

Friday — front — page 15

Add.

0+3= 3   2+4= 6   5+2= 7
1+6= 7   4+0= 4   0+5= 5
3+5= 8   6+0= 6   1+4= 5

Match the numbers that are the same.

46	97
35	46
97	64
64	35

22	11
12	22
11	12
21	21

78	80
52	46
80	52
46	78

Draw a picture of the sentence.

The cat is in the box.

A leaf is on the grass.

Put an X on the pictures that do not begin with the /v/ sound.

violin, valentine, vegetables, van, vase, hand, mosquito

back — page 15

Cut out the shapes and arrange them to form the picture. For extra fun you may glue the shapes to another piece of paper.

Friday

Add.

4	6	3	3	2	1	4	0	6	3
+6	+3	+0	+3	+6	+4	+1	+5	+1	+4
10	9	3	5	7	5	5	5	7	7

Draw a line to "cut" each shape in half.

Write the lowercase letter next to the capital.

D d   P p   B b

N n   Z z   L l

X x   J j   V v

Put an X on the pictures that do not end with the /l/ sound.

leaf   giraffe   brush   wolf

pencil sharpener   church

safe   sailor

Color the loud things red. Color the quiet things blue.

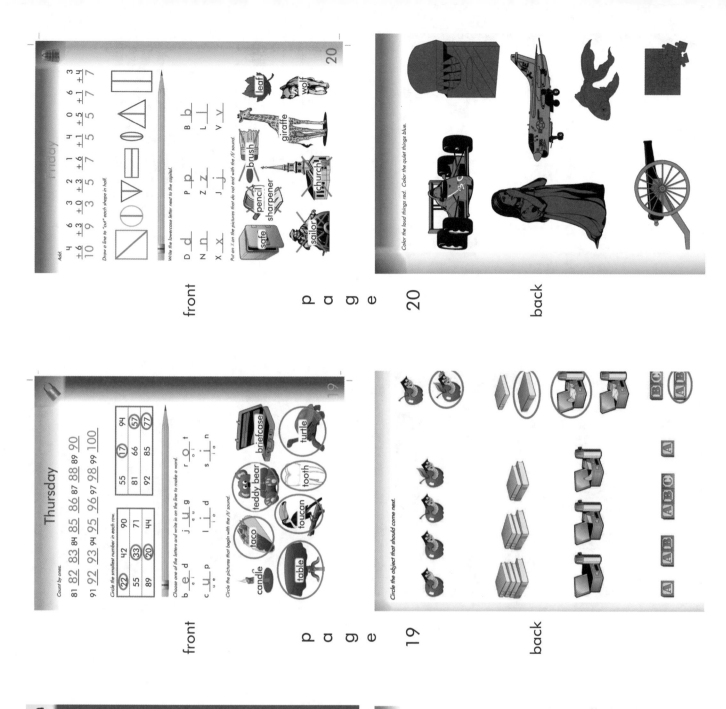

Thursday

Count by ones.

81 82 83 84 85 86 87 88 89 90

91 92 93 94 95 96 97 98 99 100

Circle the smaller number in each row.

22	42	90
55	33	71
89	20	44

55	17	94
81	66	57
92	85	77

Choose one of the letters and write in on the line to make a word.

b e d   j u g   r o t

c _ p   l _ d   s _ n

Circle the pictures that begin with the /t/ sound.

candle   taco   feddy bear   briefcase

table   toucan   tooth   turtle

Circle the object that should come next.

Wednesday

Add.

0+0= 0   3+2= 5   1+4= 5

2+5= 7   5+5= 10   6+0= 6

0+9= 9   4+2= 6   3+7= 10

Write the number that comes before and after (counting by ones).

24 25 26   38 39 40   34 35 36

20 21 22   30 31 32   36 37 38

27 28 29   21 22 23   32 33 34

Write the word on the lines under the correct picture.

tack   map   bus

map   bus   tack

Number the sentences in the order they happened.

3 Sam went to bed.

2 Sam ate his meal.

1 Sam had fun in the grass.

2 The bug ate and ate.

1 The bug is not big.

3 The bug is big.

Circle the animals that have feathers.

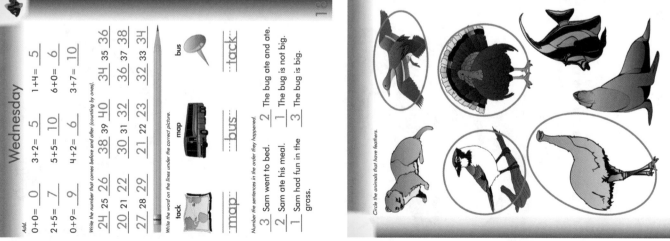

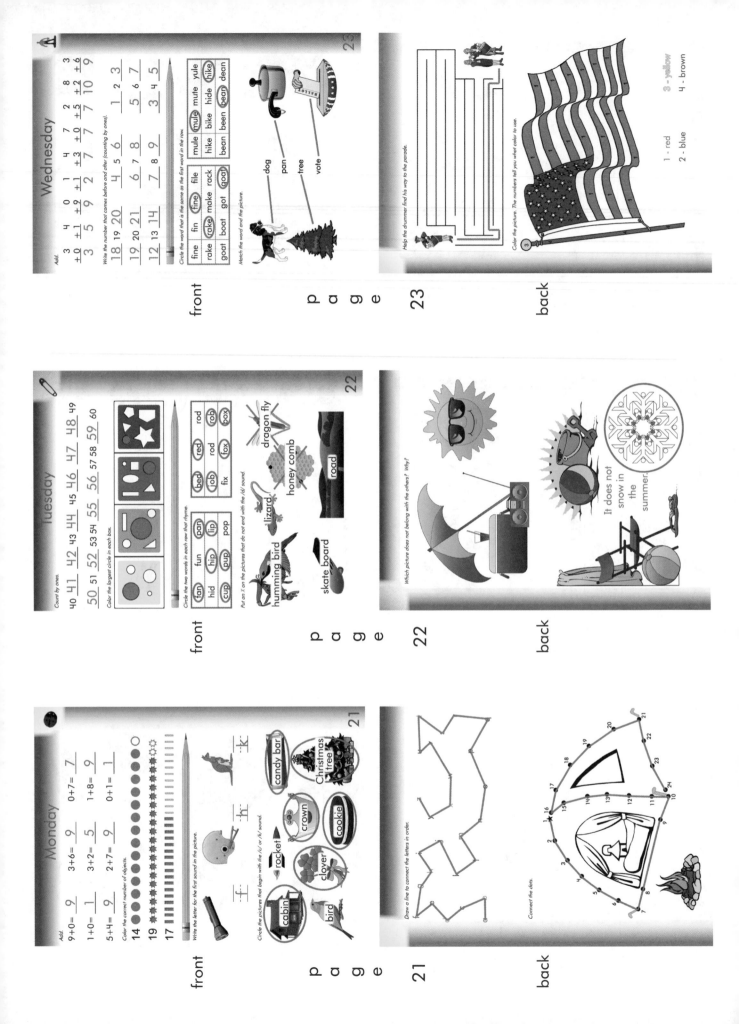

Monday (front)

front

Add.

9+0= 9   3+6= 9   0+7= 7
1+0= 1   3+2= 5   1+8= 9
5+4= 9   2+7= 9   0+1= 1

Color the correct number of objects.

14 ●●●●●●●●●●
19 ✳✳✳✳✳✳✳✳✳✳
17 ||||||||||

Write the letter for the first sound in the picture.

f   k   h

Circle the pictures that begin with the /c/ or /k/ sound.

cabin   clover   cookie   rocket   crown   bird   candy bar   Christmas tree

page 21 (back)

Draw a line to connect the letters in order.

Connect the dots.

Tuesday (front)

front

Count by ones.

40 41 42 43 44 45 46 47 48 49
50 51 52 53 54 55 56 57 58 59 60

Color the largest circle in each box.

Circle the two words in each row that rhyme.

tan   fun   pan
hid   hip   lip
cup   pup   pop

Put an X on the pictures that do not end with the /d/ sound.

dragon fly   honey comb   lizard   road   humming bird   skate board

red   rod
bed   rob   rod   box
rob   fix   fox

page 22 (back)

Which picture does not belong with the others? Why?

It does not snow in the summer.

Wednesday (front)

front

Add.

```
  3    4    0    1    7    2
 +0   +1   +9   +1   +0   +5
 ---  ---  ---  ---  ---  ---
  3    5    9    2    7    7
```

```
  4    5    6    2    8    3
 +3   +1   +1   +1   +2   +6
 ---  ---  ---  ---  ---  ---
  7    6    7    3   10    9
```

Write the number that comes before and after (counting by ones).

18 19 20
19 20 21
12 13 14
4   5   6
6   7   8
7   8   9
1   2   3
5   6   7
3   4   5

Circle the word that is the same as the first word in the row.

fine	fin	fine	file
rake	rake	make	rack
goat	boat	got	goat
mule	mule	mute	yule
hike	bike	hide	hike
bean	been	bean	dean

Match the word and the picture.

dog   pan   tree   vote

page 23 (back)

Help the drummer find his way to the parade.

Color the picture. The numbers tell you what color to use.

1 - red   3 - yellow
2 - blue   4 - brown

Monday

Add.

2	3	1	8	4	0	7	4	5
+3	+6	+5	+0	+5	+2	+2	+3	+2
5	9	6	8	9	2	9	7	7

Draw the correct number of suns in each box.

8   5   10

In each row, circle the letter that is different.

q q q **w** q
u u u **e** u
a a **f** a a
k h h h

Circle the pictures that have the /x/ sound at the end.

mail box   jack-in-the-box   fox   shell   fawn   ox   lunch box

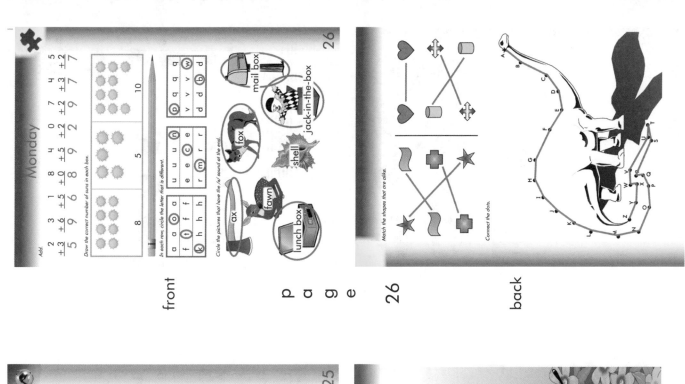

Match the shapes that are alike.

Connect the dots.

Friday

Add.

8+0= 8   4+4= 8   6+2= 8
2+6= 8   0+8= 8   3+3= 6
5+1= 6   9+0= 9   1+2= 3

Put an X on the number that is different in each row.

57	57	57	57
82	82	82	82
43	43	43	43

66	66	66
12	12	12
19	19	19

Match the upper and lower case letters.

W I U
w i u

K Y M
k y m

C O A
c o a

Put an X on the pictures that do not begin with the /r/ sound.

radish   radio   rings   owl   rolls   rose   golfer

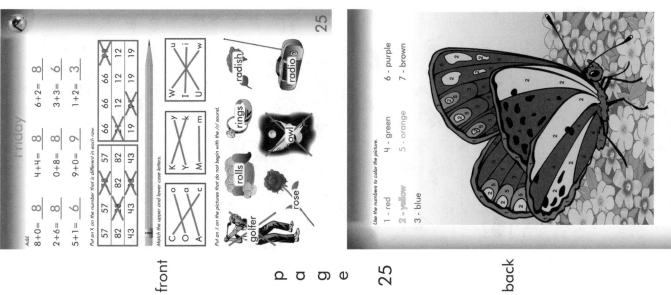

Use the numbers to color the picture.

1 - red   4 - green   6 - purple
2 - yellow   5 - orange   7 - brown
3 - blue

Thursday

Count by tens.

10 20 30 40 50 60 70 80 90 100

Write what comes next on the line.

133 133 133

Draw a picture of the word in the box.

hot   bug   leg

Circle the pictures that have the short /i/ sound in the middle of the word.

clip   butterfly   pin   parrot   scissors   conductor

Circle the sentence that tells about the picture.

Hal had a box.
Hal had a bag.

The rat is a bed.
The rat is big.

The map is big.
The van is big.

The mud is wet.
The sun is hot.

Help the man get to work.

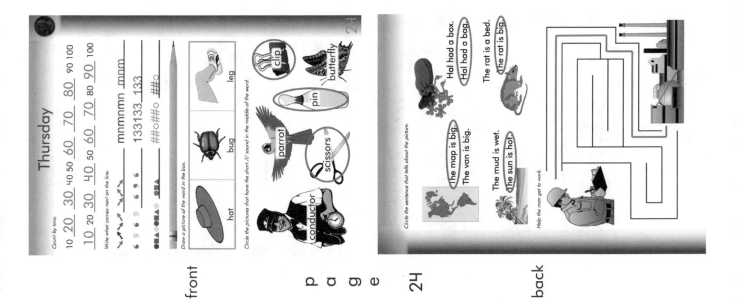

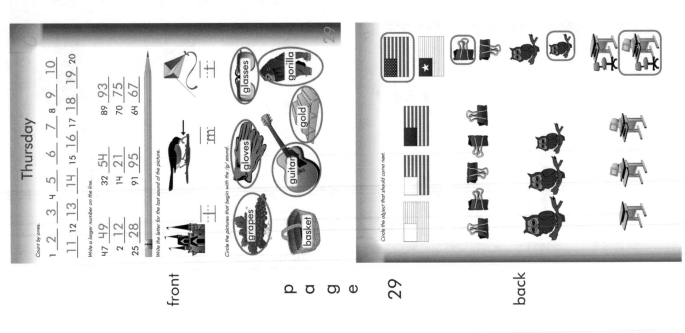

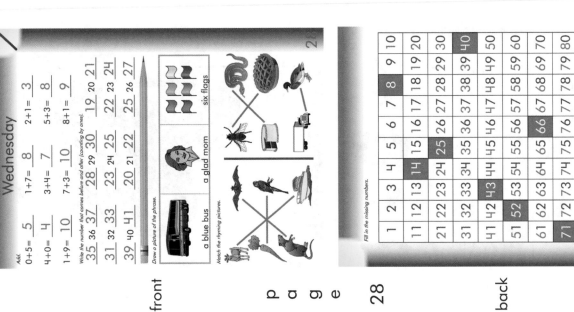

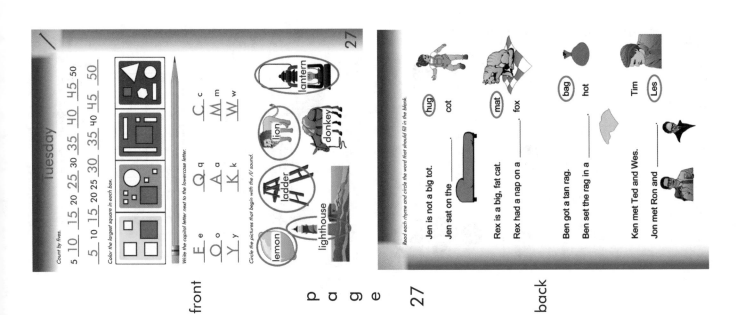

Tuesday

Count by fives.

5 __10__ 15 20 __25__ 30 __35__ __40__ __45__ __50__

5 __10__ __15__ 20 25 __30__ 35 __40__ 45 __50__

Color the largest square in each box.

Write the capital letter next to the lowercase letter:

E e   Q q   C c
Q o   A a   M m
Y y   K k   W w

Circle the pictures that begin with the /l/ sound.

lemon   lantern   ladder   lion   donkey   lighthouse

back — page 27

Read each rhyme and circle the word that should fill in the blank.

Jen is not a big tot.
Jen sat on the _____   (hug) cot

Rex is a big, fat cat.
Rex had a nap on a _____   (mat) fox

Ben got a tan rag.
Ben set the rag in a _____   (bag) hot

Ken met Ted and Wes.
Jon met Ron and _____   Tim (Les)

Wednesday

front — page 28

Add.

0+5= __5__   1+7= __8__   2+1= __3__
4+0= __4__   3+4= __7__   5+3= __8__
1+9= __10__   7+3= __10__   8+1= __9__

Write the number that comes before and after (counting by ones):

35 36 37   28 29 30   19 20 21
31 32 33   23 24 25   22 23 24
39 40 41   20 21 22   25 26 27

Draw a picture of the phrase.

a blue bus   a glad mom   six flags

Match the rhyming pictures.

back — page 28

Fill in the missing numbers.

1	2	3	4	5	6	7	8	9	10
11	12	13	14	15	16	17	18	19	20
21	22	23	24	25	26	27	28	29	30
31	32	33	34	35	36	37	38	39	40
41	42	43	44	45	46	47	48	49	50
51	52	53	54	55	56	57	58	59	60
61	62	63	64	65	66	67	68	69	70
71	72	73	74	75	76	77	78	79	80
81	82	83	84	85	86	87	88	89	90
91	92	93	94	95	96	97	98	99	100

Thursday

front — page 29

Count by ones.

1 __2__ 3 4 __5__ 6 7 __8__ __9__ __10__

__11__ 12 __13__ 14 __15__ 16 17 __18__ __19__ __20__

Write a larger number on the line.

47 __49__   32 __54__   89 __93__
2 __12__   14 __21__   70 __75__
25 __28__   91 __95__   64 __67__

Write the letter for the last sound of the picture.

__t__   __m__   __t__

Circle the pictures that begin with the /g/ sound.

grapes   gloves   glasses   basket   guitar   gold   gorilla

back — page 29

Circle the object that should come next.

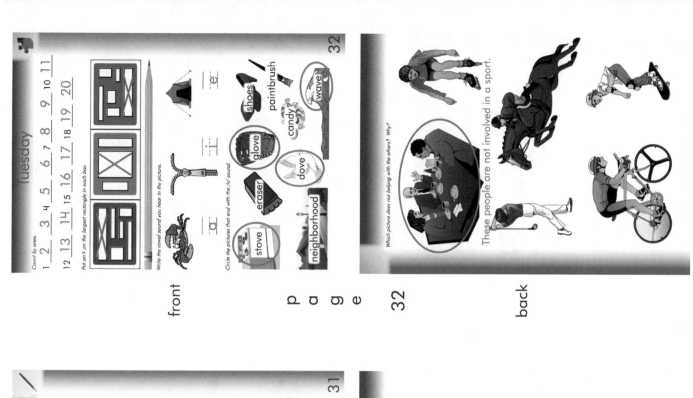

Tuesday

Count by ones.

1 2 3 4 5 6 7 8 9 10 11
12 13 14 15 16 17 18 19 20

Put an X on the largest rectangle in each box.

Write the vowel sound you hear in the picture.

__a__   __i__   __e__

Circle the pictures that end with the /v/ sound.

shoes   paintbrush   candy   glove   dove   eraser   stove   neighborhood   wave

front

p
a
g
e

32

back

Which picture does not belong with the others? Why?

These people are not involved in a sport.

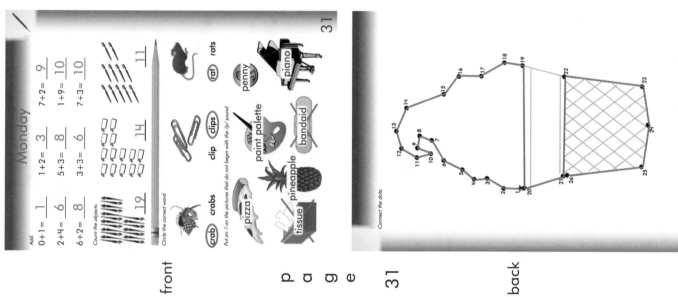

Monday

Add.

0+1= 1	1+2= 3	7+2= 9
2+4= 6	5+3= 8	1+9= 10
6+2= 8	3+3= 6	7+3= 10

Count the objects.

19   14   11

Circle the correct word.

crab crabs   rat rats   penny   clip clips   piano

Put an X on the pictures that do not begin with the /p/ sound.

pizza   pineapple   tissue   paint palette   bandaid

front

p
a
g
e

31

back

Connect the dots.

Friday

Add.

4	0	5	2	8	0	1	2	5
+5	+2	+2	+7	+1	+3	+8	+1	+5
9	2	7	9	9	3	9	3	10

Circle the shapes that have been divided in half.

Choose one of the letters and write it on the line to make a word.

p __ an   __ og   h __ ill
 p g   n l   h z

f __ un   b __ ed   m __ at
 l m   k b   w m

Circle the pictures that end with a /b/ sound.

web   dust pan   barricade   bulb   crab   tub   picture

front

p
a
g
e

30

back

Color the hot things orange. Color the cold things purple.

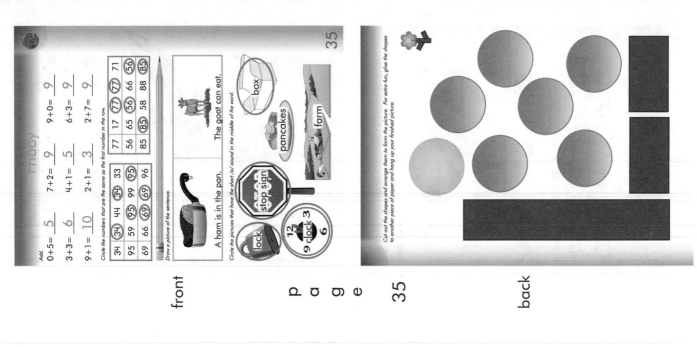

Friday

Add.

0+5= 5	7+2= 9	9+0= 9
3+3= 6	4+1= 5	6+3= 9
9+1= 10	2+1= 3	2+7= 9

Circle the numbers that are the same as the first number in the row.

34	34	34	33		77	17	77	71
95	59	99	95		56	65	56	66	56
69	66	69	96		85	85	58	88	85

Draw a picture of the sentence.

A ham is in the pan.

Circle the pictures that have the short /o/ sound in the middle of the word.

box · pancakes · farm · stop sign · lock · clock · The goat can eat.

front · p a g e 35 · back

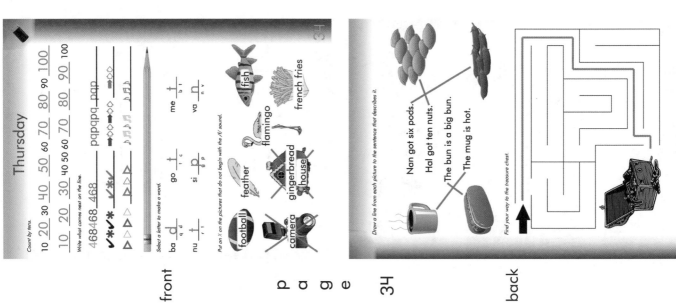

Thursday

Count by tens.

10 20 30 40 50 60 70 80 90 100

10 20 30 40 50 60 70 80 90 100

Write what comes next on the line.

468 468 468

✓*✓* ✓*✓

△▽△ △▽△

Select a letter to make a word.

ba d · go t · me t

nu t · si p · va n

Put an X on the pictures that do not begin with the /f/ sound.

football · camera · feather · flamingo · gingerbread house · fish · french fries

front · p a g e 34

Draw a line from each picture to the sentence that describes it.

Nan got six pods.
Hal got ten nuts.
The bun is a big bun.
The mug is hot.

Find your way to the treasure chest.

back

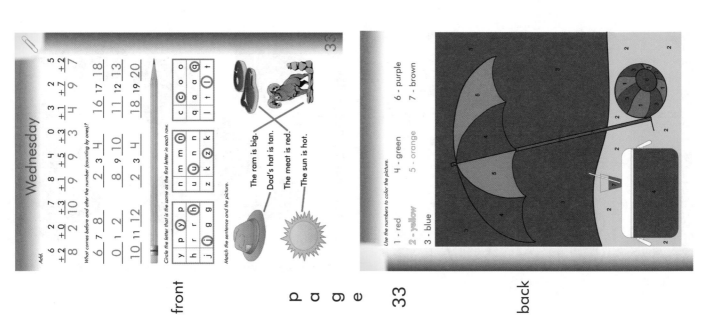

Wednesday

Add.

What comes before and after the number (counting by ones)?

Circle the letter that is the same as the first letter in each row.

Match the sentence and the picture.

The ram is big.
Dad's hat is tan.
The meat is red.
The sun is hot.

front · p a g e 33

Use the numbers to color the picture.

1 - red   4 - green   6 - purple
2 - yellow   5 - orange   7 - brown
3 - blue

back

Monday

Add.

8	5	1	5		2	7	4	3	1
+0	+1	+0	+5		+3	+1	+2	+6	+4
8	6	1	10		5	8	6	9	5

Color the correct number of objects.

18
15
13

Circle the word that is different in each row.

wig	wag	wig	wig
mad	mad	sad	mad
fell	felt	felt	felt

Put an X on the pictures that do not have the /i/ sound at the beginning.

stop	stop	stop	step
bag	beg	beg	beg
sun	fun	sun	sun

igloo dove fish Indian inchworm helicopter in

Tuesday

Count by fives.

5 10 15 20 25 30 35 40 45 50
55 60 65 70 75 80 85 90 95 100

Color the smallest triangle in each box.

Number the days of the week in order.

1 Sunday   5 Thursday   7 Saturday
4 Wednesday   2 Monday   3 Tuesday
                              6 Friday

Circle the pictures that begin with the short /a/ sound.

apple   alligator   ant   watch   astronaut   diploma   eagle

Wednesday

Add.

7+2= 9	5+0= 5	3+3= 6
1+7= 8	6+3= 9	4+1= 5
2+2= 4	0+2= 2	3+0= 3

Write the number that comes before and after (counting by ones).

32 33 34	31 32 33	36 37 38
26 27 28	38 39 40	28 29 30
35 36 37	33 34 35	27 28 29

Write the word on the line under the correct picture.

tent   hen   pig

hen   pig   tent

Number the sentences in the order they happened.

3 The plant is big.
1 See Jill plant the seed.
2 The rain fell on the seed.

2 A cat came.
3 The rat ran and ran.
1 A rat sat on a mat.

Connect the dots.

Circle the sentence that finishes each story.

1. Max is Kim's pet.
2. Max can run and sit.
3. Max can beg.
4. Max is a fun pet.
or
4. Max is a big cat.

1. Jen's top had a rip.
2. Can Mom fix the rip?
3. Mom got Jen's top.
4. The rip is a leg.
or
4. Mom did fix the rip in Jen's top.

1. Mom had a tot.
2. The tot is Ben.
3. The tot can sip and sip.
4. Ben can sip and sip.
or
4. Ben is hot and sad.

Circle the animals that live in water.

Add.

1+3 = 4	2+6 = 8	4+2 = 6
3+7 = 10	1+7 = 8	3+1 = 4
2+0 = 2	0+8 = 8	1+5 = 6

Draw the correct number of squares.

7   6   10

Write the letter for the first sound in the picture.

_t_   _y_   _b_

Put an X on the pictures that do not start with the /m/ sound.

mail   taxi   monkey   money   medals   motorcycle   grasshopper

Color all the arrows pointing to the left.

Connect the dots.

Add.

0	5	2	0	3	2	9	6	4
+8	+3	+6	+3	+4	+3	+1	+2	+5
8	8	8	3	7	5	10	8	9

Color one half of each shape.

Write the capital letter next to the lowercase letter:

H h   I i   F f
R r   D d   P p
B b   N n   Z z

Circle the pictures that end with the /t/ sound.

paint   rabbit   queen   trumpet   hamster   train   sailboat

Circle the sentence that tells about the picture.

The ant got it. / The ox got it.

It is hot and wet. / It can pop up at a tot.

It has red on it. / It has tan on it.

The rat bit it. / The cat can hit it.

Help the ship find its way to land.

Count by ones.

61 62 63 64 65 66 67 68 69 70
71 72 73 74 75 76 77 78 79 80

Circle the smallest number in each row.

46	18	59
35	47	27
41	83	26

52	91	60
76	14	38
82	30	25

Choose one of the letters and write it on the line to make a word.

d o g   (e / u)   k i d   (o / a)   t o p   (o / e)
f u n   m o p   v a n

Put an X on the pictures that do not begin with the /d/ sound.

fireman   dime   duck   car   drums   backpack   doughnut   dinosaur

Draw a line to the object that should come next.

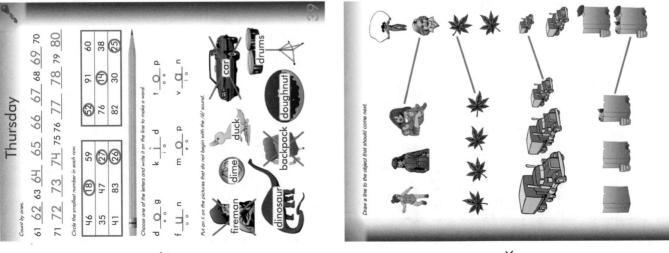

Thursday

Count by tens.
10 20 30 40 50 60 70 80 90 100
10 20 30 40 50 60 70 80 90 100

Draw what comes next on the line.

88888 888
rstrst rst

Draw a picture of the word in the box.

| bun | dog | cake |

Put an X on the pictures that do not have the short /u/ sound in the middle of the word.

brush · wasp nest · paperclips · mustard · duck · window · drum

front

p a g e 44

back

Color the wiggly or fast things yellow. Color the still or slow things brown.

Wednesday

Add.

1	5	3	0	1	6	8	2
+0	+4	+2	+1	+1	+1	+2	+4
1	9	5	1	4	7	10	6

What comes before and after the number?

7 8 9   12 13 14   13 14 15
1 2 3   11 12 13   15 16 17
4 5 6   9 10 11   19 20 21

Circle the word that is the same as the first word in the row.

pen	pen	pin	pet
hit	hat	hit	hot
sad	sat	sag	sad

top	tap	mop	top
get	get	got	jet
bud	mud	mad

Match the word and the picture.

cake
hot dog
jet
mule

front

p a g e 43

back

Use the numbers to color the picture.

1 - red   4 - green   6 - purple
2 - yellow   5 - orange   7 - brown
3 - blue

Tuesday

Count by ones.
20 21 22 23 24 25 26 27 28 29
30 31 32 33 34 35 36 37 38 39 40

In each box, put an X on the shape that does not belong.

Match the rhyming words.

sun   win
pin   cot
hot   fun

ten   tell
had   men
bell   lad

Circle the pictures that end with the /s/ sound.

magnifying glass · scissors · rhinoceros · suitcase · stapler · hawk · slide

front

p a g e 42

back

Which picture does not belong with the others? Why?

This is not a tool.

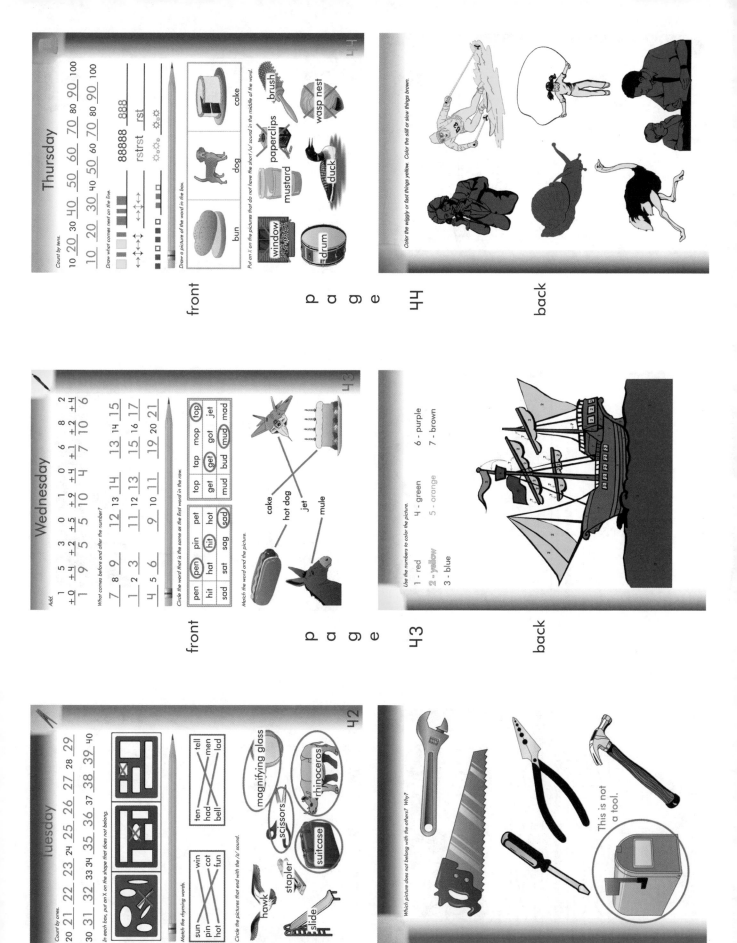

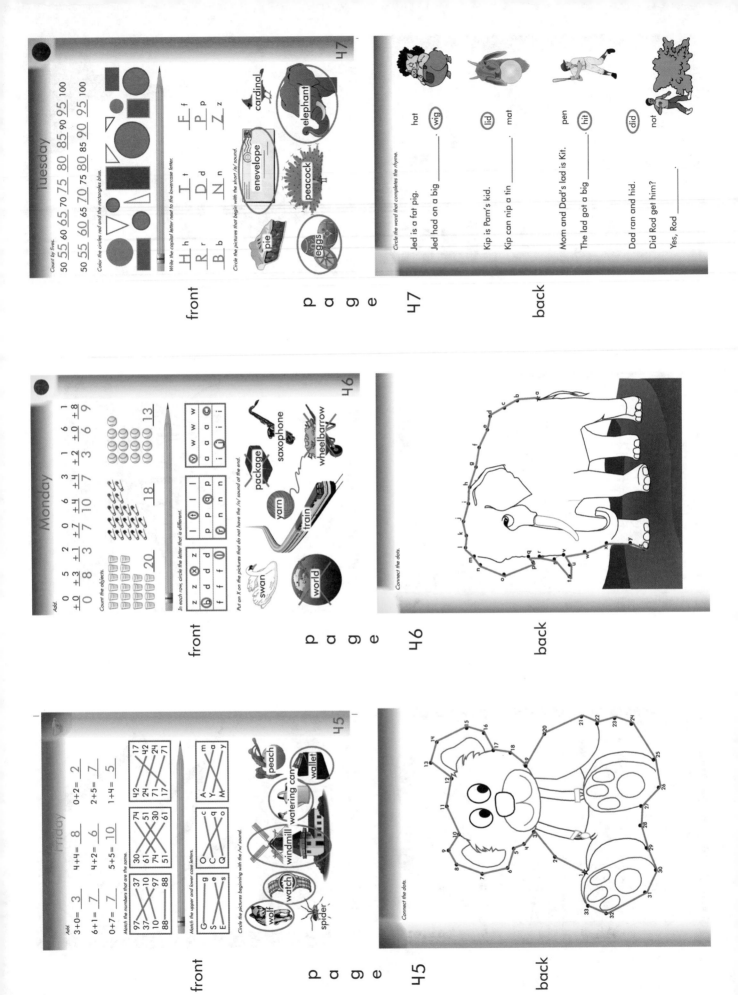

Tuesday — front (page 47)

Count by fives.

50 55 60 65 70 75 80 85 90 95 100

Color the circles red and the rectangles blue.

Write the capital letter next to the lowercase letter:

H h   I t   F f
R r   D d   P p
B b   N n   Z z

Circle the pictures that begin with the short /e/ sound.

envelope   peacock   eggs   pie   cardinal   elephant

Tuesday — back (page 47)

Circle the word that completes the rhyme.

Jed is a fat pig.
Jed had on a big _____ .   hat   (wig)

Kip is Pam's kid.
Kip can nip a tin _____ .   (lid)   mat

Mom and Dad's lad is Kit.
The lad got a big _____ .   pen   (hit)

Dad ran and hid.
Did Rod get him?
Yes, Rod _____ .   (did)   not

Monday — front (page 46)

Add

0   5   2   0   6   3   1
+0 +3 +1 +7 +4 +4 +6
0   8   3   7 10   7

Count the objects.

20   18   13

In each row, circle the letter that is different.

z z Ⓩ z
l Ⓣ l l
Ⓟ p p
Ⓝ n n

Ⓥ w w w
Ⓞ a a a
i i Ⓣ i

Put an X on the pictures that do not have the /n/ sound at the end.

swan   world   yarn   package   train   saxophone   wheelbarrow

Monday — back (page 46)

Connect the dots.

Friday — front (page 45)

Add

3+0= 3   4+4= 8   0+2= 2
6+1= 7   4+2= 6   2+5= 7
0+7= 7   5+5= 10   1+4= 5

Match the numbers that are the same.

97 — 37
37 — 10
10 — 97
88 — 88

30 — 74
51 — 61
74 — 30
61 — 51

17 — 42
42 — 24
24 — 71
71 — 17

Match the upper and lower case letters.

G — g
S — e
E — s

O — c
C — q
Q — o

A — a
Y — y
M — m

Circle the pictures beginning with the /w/ sound.

wolf   watch   spider   windmill   watering can   wallet   peach

Friday — back (page 45)

Connect the dots.

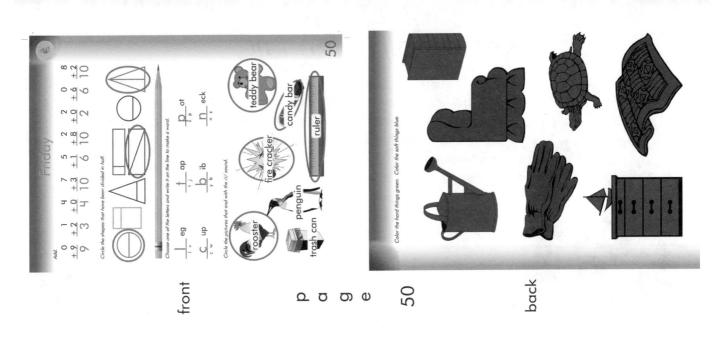

Friday

Add:

0	1	4	7	5	2	2	0	8
+9	+2	+0	+3	+1	+8	+0	+6	+2
9	3	4	10	6	10	2	6	10

Circle the shapes that have been divided in half.

Choose one of the letters and write it on the line to make a word.

___ eg (l, v) ___ ap (t, j) ___ ot (s, p)

___ up (c, w) ___ ib (y, b) ___ eck (n, z)

Circle the pictures that end with the /r/ sound.

rooster penguin trash can fire cracker candy bar teddy bear ruler

front

p a g e 50

back

Color the hard things green. Color the soft things blue.

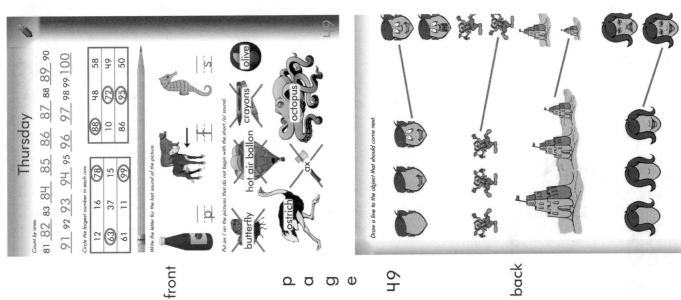

Thursday

Count by ones.

81 82 83 84 85 86 87 88 89 90

91 92 93 94 95 96 97 98 99 100

Circle the largest number in each row.

88	48	58
10	72	49
86	95	50

12	16	78
63	37	15
61	11	99

Write the letter for the last sound of the picture.

___ s   ___ f   ___ p   olive

Put an X on the pictures that do not begin with the short /o/ sound.

crayons octopus hot air balloon ax butterfly ostrich

front

p a g e 49

back

Draw a line to the object that should come next.

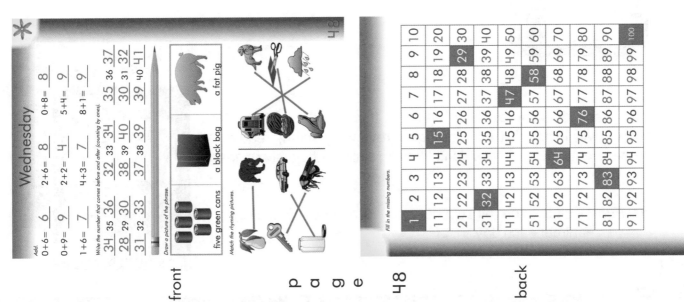

Wednesday

Add

0+6= 6   2+6= 8   0+8= 8

0+9= 9   2+2= 4   5+4= 9

1+6= 7   4+3= 7   8+1= 9

Write the number that comes before and after (counting by ones).

34 35 36   32 33 34   35 36 37

28 29 30   38 39 40   30 31 32

31 32 33   37 38 39   39 40 41

Draw a picture of the phrase.

five green cans | a black bag | a fat pig

Match the rhyming pictures.

front

p a g e 48

back

Fill in the missing numbers.

1	2	3	4	5	6	7	8	9	10
11	12	13	14	15	16	17	18	19	20
21	22	23	24	25	26	27	28	29	30
31	32	33	34	35	36	37	38	39	40
41	42	43	44	45	46	47	48	49	50
51	52	53	54	55	56	57	58	59	60
61	62	63	64	65	66	67	68	69	70
71	72	73	74	75	76	77	78	79	80
81	82	83	84	85	86	87	88	89	90
91	92	93	94	95	96	97	98	99	100

Know it all in the fall . . .

Summer Book K is for students entering kindergarten (K5). It contains fifty pages of daily work. The front of each page contains written activities for the child to complete. The back of each page suggests fun games and activities as well as tips for parents. A complete answer key is included.

Upper- and lower-case magnetic letters and numbers are included with the book as well as shapes in a wide variety of colors.

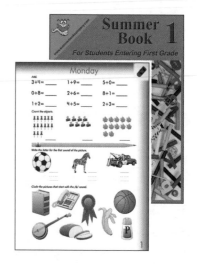

Summer Book 1 is for students entering first grade. Students will know it all in the fall by thoroughly reviewing reading, math, phonics and thinking skills. Fifty daily pages and answer key.

Special Fun: Develop visual tracking skills by playing "I spy" each day. The item of the day is on the top corner of the page and can be found on either the front or back cover of the book.

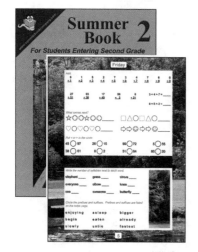

Summer Book 2 is for students entering second grade. Know it all in the fall by thoroughly reviewing math, reading comprehension, writing, phonics and thinking skills. Fifty daily pages and answer key.

Special Fun: Encourage patience, persistence, and visual skills while going through the maze on the back of each page.

Summer Book 3 is for students entering third grade. Students will know it all in the fall by thoroughly reviewing math, reading comprehension, writing, English and thinking skills. Fifty daily pages and answer key.

Special Fun: "Visit the zoo" all summer and learn about a different animal each day.

www.summerbookcompany.com or 877-684-8502

. . . with only one book!

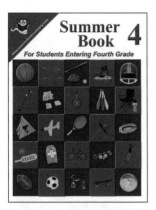

Summer Book 4 is for students entering fourth grade. Contains fifty daily pages and an answer key.

Extras: Enjoy learning about many different sports and outdoor activities.

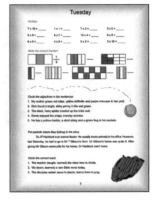

Summer Books 4-7 thoroughly review math, reading comprehension, grammar, writing, and thinking skills. History, health and science are also refreshed.

Summer Book 5 is for students entering fifth grade. Contains fifty daily pages and an answer key.

Extras: Learn about different rocks and beautiful gemstones (in the new edition in '08). Also practice map skills and shopping wisdom.

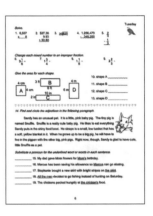

Summer Book 6 is for students entering sixth grade. Contains fifty daily pages and an answer key.

Extras: Discover outer space, planets, astronauts and trips to the moon.

Summer Book 7 is for students entering seventh grade. Contains fifty daily pages and an answer key.

Extras: Improve world geography skills by learning about a new country each day and identifying it on the world map.

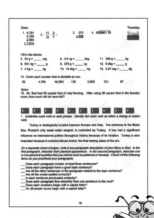

Reading Comprehension for Everyone

With bright, colorful pictures, the *Summerbook Readers* are a delight for beginners. The short-vowel words and short sentences help new readers gain confidence quickly. Paperback, 40 pages each. (set of 3) 62 reproducible worksheets accompany the books. Grade K

Non-fiction Reading Comprehension offers brief nonfiction passages about science, geography, or history topics. Students answer multiple-choice and short-answer questions to build seven essential comprehension skills. Grades: 1-6

Visit our website, www.summerbookcompany.com to see other reading comprehension materials.

Strategies That Work: Comprehension Practice develops reading comprehension skills with strategies that work! Each reproducible page includes literary or factual text, followed by multiple-choice, true-false, short answer, or other types of questions. Grades: 7-8

☞ *English grammar made easy . . . finally!* ☜

Step-by-Step Grammar Volume I: Basic Grammar teaches the basic eight parts of speech. It also teaches diagraming, compound sentences, prepositional phrases, and verb phrases. This book is written to be used by fifth and sixth graders who are struggling with grammar. *However, anyone who lacks a solid understanding of the basic eight parts of speech will benefit from this approach.* 119 pages. Grades 4+

Grammar Study Cards help students memorize basic definitions and lists.

Step-by-Step Grammar Volume II: Basic Usage was written to go with *Volume I: Basic Grammar* but can be used independently. This second book teaches punctuation usage, subject-verb agreement, plurals, possessive forms and other sentence necessities. It helps your child understand the rules for written English and learn how to put a sentence together properly and punctuate it correctly. 190 pages. Grades 4+

To see sample pages or download other free pages, visit our website, www.summerbookcompany.com.

Bend your brain and THINK!

More fun than mindless coloring books, *Thinker Doodles* develop organized analysis and motor skills needed for success in reading, writing, and mathematics. Just add your creative child and crayons! Reproducible. Grades: PreK-1

Mind Benders Develops the logic, reading comprehension, and mental organization skills vital to achieving high grades and top test scores in all subjects. Also great for helping your child develop real-life, problem-solving skills. Answer key included. Reproducible. Grades: PreK-6

Think-A-Minutes This collection of popular quick, fun thinking puzzles and games develops a variety of critical and creative thinking skills for top academic performance in all subjects. Answer key included. Reproducible. Grades: 2-8

ThinkAnalogies Build vocabulary and reading comprehension skills! Your child will classify word groups, form pairs of related items, then identify and classify types of relationships. Finally, select and supply words and word pairs to complete analogies. Includes answers and a fun reward game. Reproducible. Grades: 3-8

Building Thinking Skills Levels 1 and 2 provide highly effective verbal and nonverbal reasoning activities to improve students' vocabulary, reading, writing, math, logic, and figural-spatial skills, as well as their visual and auditory processing. This exceptional series provides a solid foundation for academic excellence in any assessment. Reproducible. Grades 2-6

Building Thinking Skills Level 3, separates the verbal and figural exercises to provide more in-depth practice in each area. Answer key included for each book. Reproducible. Grades: 7-12

Math, English, geography – practice them all with dice!

Educational dice provide drills and games to teach and reenforce an amazing array of concepts across the curriculum. Check out the website to see all the options for grades K-12.

C4

Become a Math Master

Children need lots of drill on the basic math facts to truly master them. These *reproducible* books will help make it easy for you to give your child all the drill he or she needs.

The Basic Facts Drill Book for Addition and Subtraction drills 0+0 through 9+9 and the corresponding subtraction problems. 120 pages.

The Basic Facts Drill Book for Multiplication and Division drills 0x0 through 12x12 and the corresponding division problems. 120 pages.

Complete the Picture Math Levels 1, 2 and 3 ask your child to solve an engaging word problem that focuses on reading comprehension and mathematical reasoning. Then your child will complete an animal picture. These quick, boredom-busting activities can be used at home and on trips. Reproducible. Grades: 1-3

Math Word Problems Levels A, B and C Help your child conquer the "dreaded" math word problem. Each problem requires its own thinking/problem solving approach rather than mindlessly applying the same process to entire groups of problems. Example problems and answer key. Reproducible. Grades: 4-8

Pre-Algebra makes sure your child is ready for Algebra in the fall. Topics include integers; fractions; decimals; estimation; ratios, proportions, and percents; square roots; statistics and probability. Also includes assessment tests, and an answer key. Reproducible. Grades: 7+

Help your high school student keep his brain in gear after Algebra I, II or Geometry. More than just numbers to crunch, these books offer multi-step problems that develop your student's problem-solving skills. Fun activities boost competence, confidence, and test scores while helping students make the transition to higher level mathematics. Reproducible. Grades: 9+

Miscellaneous

Magnetic Uppercase and Lowercase Letters and Numbers

Soft, finger-friendly magnetic letters and numbers make reading, spelling and math more fun. 26 letters or numbers per pack. Grades: PreK+

Magnetic Dry-Erase Board

This light metal board makes it convenient to work with magnetic letters at a desk or in a lap. The dry-erase surface multiplies its usefulness. (Board only.) Grades: PreK+

Stetro Pencil Grip

This soft, molded grip helps your child hold a pencil or crayon correctly. Works with the right or left hand. Grades: PreK+

Visit our website, www.summerbookcompany.com to see other educational materials.

C5